LARGE PRINT
BRAIN TRAINING
PUZZLES
EASY TO READ PUZZLES

ARCTURUS

ARCTURUS

This edition published in 2019 by Arcturus Publishing Limited
26/27 Bickels Yard, 151–153 Bermondsey Street,
London SE1 3HA.

Copyright © Arcturus Holdings Limited
Puzzles copyright © Puzzle Press Ltd

ISBN: 978-1-78888-692-5
AD006726NT

Printed in China

Contents

Puzzles:

Warm up with these puzzles

Puzzles to set you thinking

Exercise your brain

Hone your skills with these teasers

Give your mind a real work-out

Strictly for the initiated

Solutions 🔑

Domino Placement

A standard set of 28 dominoes has been laid out as shown.

Can you draw in the edges of them all?

The check-box is provided as an aid, and the domino already placed will help.

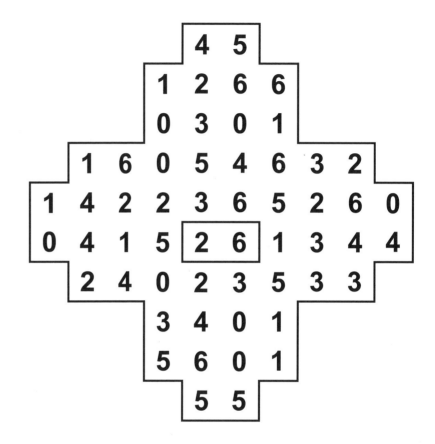

0-0	0-1	0-2	0-3	0-4	0-5	0-6	1-1	1-2	1-3	1-4	1-5	1-6	2-2

2-3	2-4	2-5	2-6	3-3	3-4	3-5	3-6	4-4	4-5	4-6	5-5	5-6	6-6
			✔										

Isolate

Draw walls to partition the grid into areas (some walls are already drawn in for you). Each area must contain two circles, area sizes must match those numbers shown above the grid and each '+' must be linked to at least two walls.

3,   3,   6,   6,   7

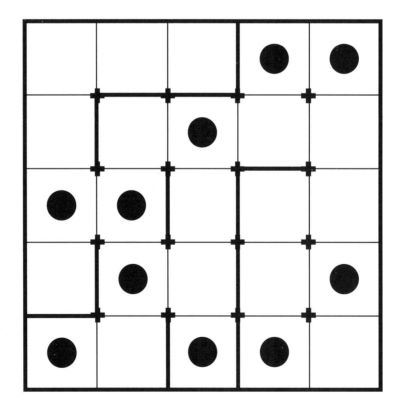

Shape Up

Every row and column in this grid originally contained one circle, one diamond, one square, one triangle and two blank squares, although not necessarily in that order.

Every symbol with a black arrow refers to the first of the four symbols encountered when moving in the direction of the arrow. Every symbol with a white arrow refers to the second of the four symbols encountered in the direction of the arrow.

Can you complete the original grid?

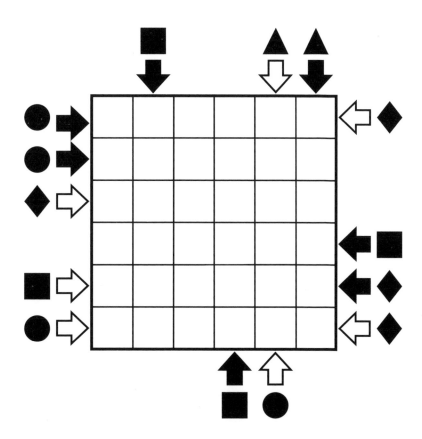

Total Concentration

The blank squares below should be filled with whole numbers between 1 and 40 inclusive, any of which may occur more than once, or not at all.

The numbers in every horizontal row add up to the totals on the right, as do the two long diagonal lines; whilst those in every vertical column add up to the totals along the bottom.

								109
14	25	11		37	32	34	2	164
		13	5	34	25	2	26	126
35	26		6	5	1	22		159
1	18	21	34	40				163
26	21			19		19	11	180
37		30	34		34	2	24	188
15	1	37	38		20	6	4	151
	12		33		21	10	4	116
144	130	182	186	198	174	122	111	161

5

Telling the Time

Draw in the missing hands on the final clock.

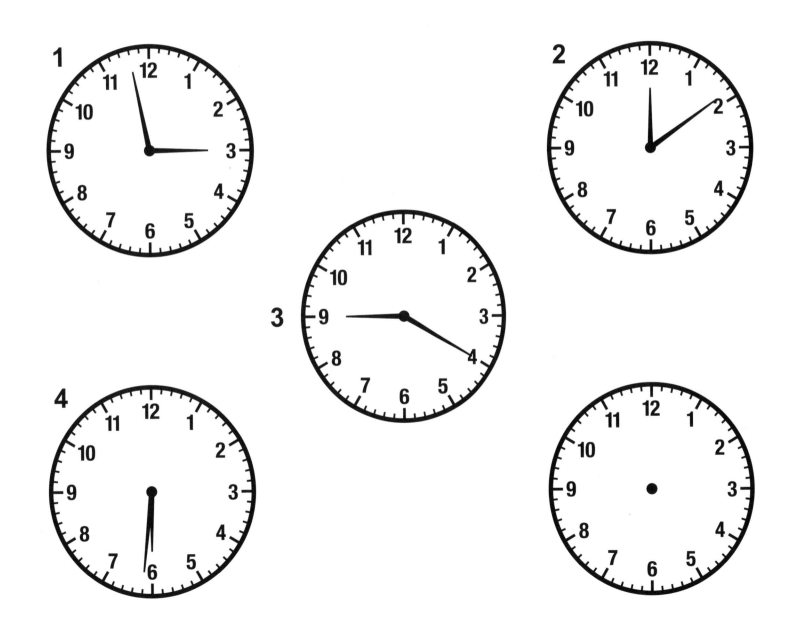

Hexagony

Can you place the hexagons into the grid, so that where any hexagon touches another along a straight line, the number in both triangles is the same? No rotation of any hexagon is allowed!

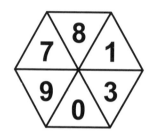

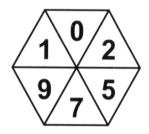

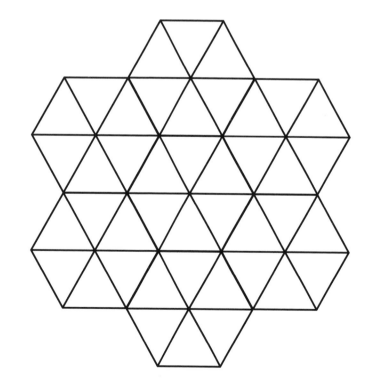

Ls in Place

Twelve L-shapes like the ones here need to be inserted in the grid and each L has one hole in it.

There are three pieces of each of the four kinds shown here and any piece may be turned or flipped over before being put in the grid. No pieces of the same kind touch, even at a corner.

The pieces fit together so well that you cannot see any spaces between them; only the holes show.

Can you tell where the Ls are?

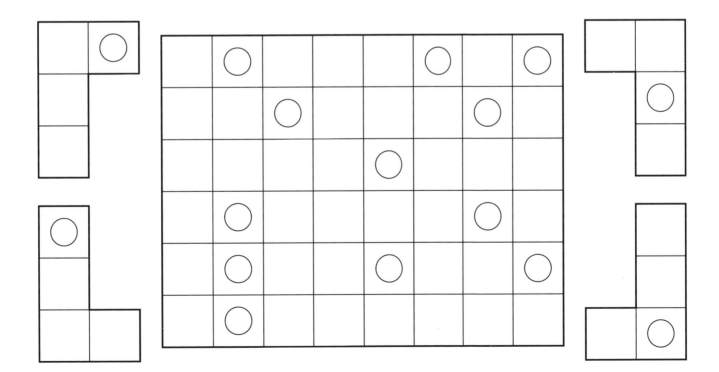

Coin Collecting

In this puzzle, an amateur coin collector has been out with his metal detector, searching for booty. He didn't have time to dig up all the coins he found, so has made a grid map, showing their locations, in the hope that if he loses the map, at least no-one else will understand it…

Those squares containing numbers are empty, but where a number appears in a square, it indicates how many coins are located in the squares (up to a maximum of eight) surrounding the numbered one, touching it at any corner or side. There is only one coin in any individual square.

Place a circle into every square containing a coin.

	0				1	2			
				2				1	
1		1				2		3	
				1		1			
	0		1				2	4	
2				4			3		
						5			
		2			4			3	
	3			2				0	
1		1			1		1		

9

Latin Square

The grid should be filled with numbers from 1 to 6, so that each number appears just once in every row and column.

The clues refer to the digit totals in the squares, eg A 1 2 3 = 6 means that the numbers in squares A1, A2 and A3 add up to 6.

	A	B	C	D	E	F
1						
2						
3						
4						
5						
6						

1 E 3 4 5 = 12

2 F 4 5 = 7

3 B C D 1 = 6

4 B C 2 = 8

5 A B 3 = 4

6 A B 4 = 9

7 C D 5 = 7

8 C D 6 = 11

9 A 1 2 = 7

10 B 5 6 = 7

11 C 3 4 = 8

Simple as A, B, C?

Each of the small squares in the grid below contains either A, B or C. Each row, column, and diagonal line of six squares has exactly two of each letter.

Can you tell the letter in each square?

	1	2	3	4	5	6
1						
2						
3						
4						
5						
6						

Across

1 The Bs are further right than the As.

2 Each B is directly next to and right of a C.

3 The As are further right than the Bs.

4 The As are further right than the Bs.

5 The Cs are not in adjacent squares.

6 The Bs are further right than the As.

Down

1 The Cs are between the As.

2 The Bs are higher than the Cs.

3 The Bs are lower than the Cs.

4 The As are between the Bs.

6 The Bs are lower than the Cs.

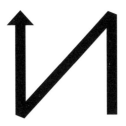

11 Zigzag

The object of this puzzle is to trace a single path from the top left corner to the bottom right corner of the grid, moving through all of the cells in either a horizontal, vertical or diagonal direction.

Every cell must be entered once only and your path should take you through the numbers in the sequence 1-2-3-4-5-6-1-2-3-4-5-6, etc.

Can you find the way?

1	2	5	6	2	3
3	4	4	2	1	4
1	5	3	1	5	1
2	6	6	4	6	2
3	4	5	3	4	3
5	6	1	2	5	6

Battleships

Can you place the vessels into the diagram? Some parts of vessels or sea squares have already been filled in. A number to the right or below a row or column refers to the number of occupied squares in that row or column.

Any vessel may be positioned horizontally or vertically, but no part of a vessel touches part of any other vessel, either horizontally, vertically or diagonally.

Empty Area of Sea:

Aircraft Carrier:

Battleships:

Cruisers:

Submarines:

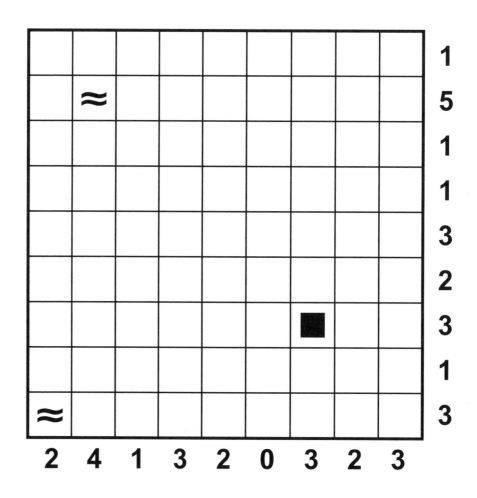

Slitherlink

Draw a single continuous loop, by connecting the dots.
No line may cross the path of another.

The figure inside each set of any four surrounding dots
indicates the total number of surrounding lines.

```
.   .   .   .   .   .   .   .   .   .   .   .
              3   1     1   2
.   .   .   .   .   .   .   .   .   .   .   .
        1   1                   0   2
.   .   .   .   .   .   .   .   .   .   .   .
  2           1           1           2
.   .   .   .   .   .   .   .   .   .   .   .
  2   1   0             3   1
.   .   .   .   .   .   .   .   .   .   .   .
  2       1   1       3   1       1
.   .   .   .   .   .   .   .   .   .   .   .
        1   2                   1
.   .   .   .   .   .   .   .   .   .   .   .
            1   3   1   2         1
.   .   .   .   .   .   .   .   .   .   .   .
          2   2
.   .   .   .   .   .   .   .   .   .   .   .
  3   3   2       1       1       1   2
.   .   .   .   .   .   .   .   .   .   .   .
            1                 1   1
.   .   .   .   .   .   .   .   .   .   .   .
  3       3   1           1   0       2
.   .   .   .   .   .   .   .   .   .   .   .
            1           3   3
.   .   .   .   .   .   .   .   .   .   .   .
```

Combiku

Each horizontal row and vertical column should contain different shapes and different numbers.

Every square will contain one number and one shape and no combination may be repeated anywhere else in the puzzle.

◇ 1   ○ 2   ☆ 3   ⬡ 4   ☐ 5

⬡3	◇4			2
☆5				☐3
				5
		◇3	☆4	

Mind Over Matter

Given that the letters are valued 1-26 according to their places in the alphabet, can you crack the mystery code to reveal the missing letter?

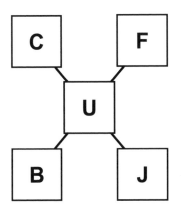

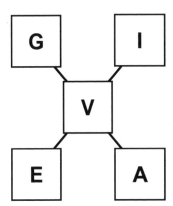

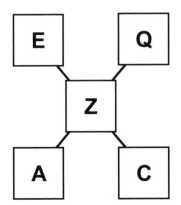

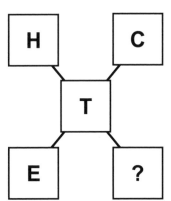

16

★

Tile Twister

Place the eight tiles into the puzzle grid so that all adjacent numbers on each tile match up. Tiles may be rotated through 360 degrees, but none may be flipped over.

2	1
4	3

2	3
2	1

4	4
2	3

2	2
4	2

3	1
3	4

		4	2		
		3	2		

3	3
1	4

4	1
2	1

2	2
3	3

It Doesn't Add Up

In the square below, change the positions of six numbers, one per horizontal row, vertical column and long diagonal line of six smaller squares, in such a way that the numbers in each row, column and long diagonal line total exactly 96.

Any number may appear more than once in a row, column or line.

14	9	10	23	14	14
25	26	18	21	30	4
22	9	12	28	21	10
21	9	30	4	17	24
9	8	6	11	32	6
14	23	26	2	10	14

Pyramid Plus

Every brick in this pyramid contains a number which is the sum of the two numbers below it, so that F=A+B, etc.

Just work out the missing numbers!

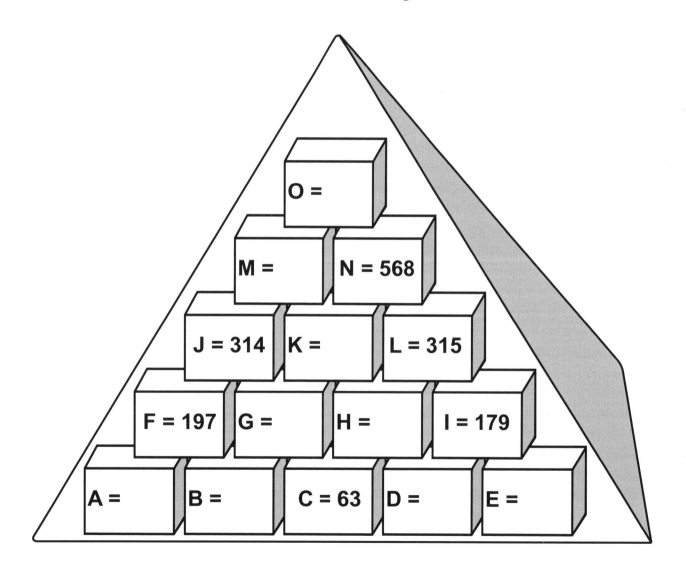

O =

M = N = 568

J = 314 K = L = 315

F = 197 G = H = I = 179

A = B = C = 63 D = E =

Treasure Hunt

The chart gives directions to a hidden treasure behind the black square in the grid. Move the indicated number of spaces north, south, east and west (eg 4N means move four squares north) stopping at every square once only to arrive there. At which square should you start?

N

W

E

1S	1E	2W	2W	1W
1E	1E	1E	1S	1N
2E	1S	■	1E	1S
1S	2E	2W	1W	1S
2N	2N	1E	2W	2W

S

Futoshiki

Fill the grid so that every horizontal row and vertical column contains the numbers 1-5.

The "greater than" or "less than" signs indicate where a number is larger or smaller than that in the adjacent square.

		< 3		
	3			2
	2	⌄		
5				
		⌄	^	

Eliminator

Every oval shape in this diagram contains a different letter of the alphabet from A to K inclusive. Use the clues to determine their locations. Reference in the clues to 'due' means in any location along the same horizontal or vertical line.

1 The A is further south than the B, further east than the F, further north than the G, and further west than the E.

2 The B is further south than the D, but further north than the H.

3 The C is next to and south of the H, which is further east than the I, which is next to and south of the J.

4 The D is next to and north of the K, which is next to and east of the J.

5 The G is next to and south of the E.

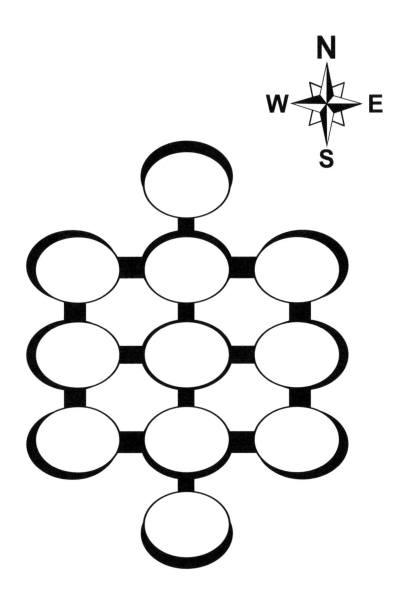

Sum Circle

Fill the three empty circles with the symbols +, − and x in some order, to make a sum which totals the central number. Each symbol must be used once and calculations are made in the direction of travel (clockwise).

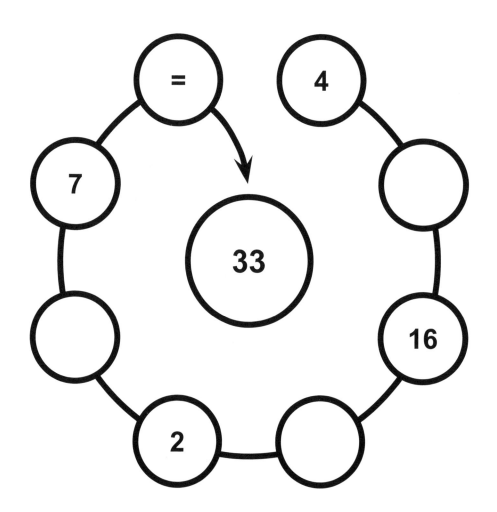

Spot Numbers

The numbers at the top and on the left side show the quantity of single-digit numbers (1-9) used in that row and column. The numbers at the bottom and on the right show the sum of the digits.

A number may appear more than once in a row or column, but no numbers are in squares that touch, even at a corner.

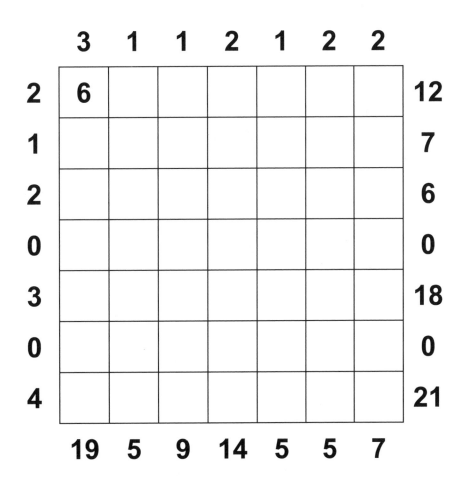

	3	1	1	2	1	2	2	
2	6							12
1								7
2								6
0								0
3								18
0								0
4								21
	19	5	9	14	5	5	7	

One to Nine

Using the numbers below, complete these six equations (three reading across and three reading downwards). Every number is used once.

1   2   3   4   5

6   7   8   9

	+		x		=	117
−	■	−	■	x		
	x		+		=	5
+	■	x	■	+		
	+		−		=	3
=		=		=		
13		12		34		

Domino Placement

A standard set of 28 dominoes has been laid out as shown.

Can you draw in the edges of them all?

The check-box is provided as an aid, and the domino already placed will help.

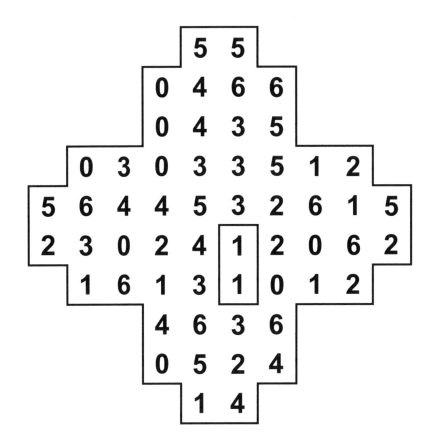

0-0	0-1	0-2	0-3	0-4	0-5	0-6	1-1	1-2	1-3	1-4	1-5	1-6	2-2
							✔						

2-3	2-4	2-5	2-6	3-3	3-4	3-5	3-6	4-4	4-5	4-6	5-5	5-6	6-6

Isolate

Draw walls to partition the grid into areas (some walls are already drawn in for you). Each area must contain two circles, area sizes must match those numbers shown above the grid and each '+' must be linked to at least two walls.

3, 3, 3, 5, 5, 6

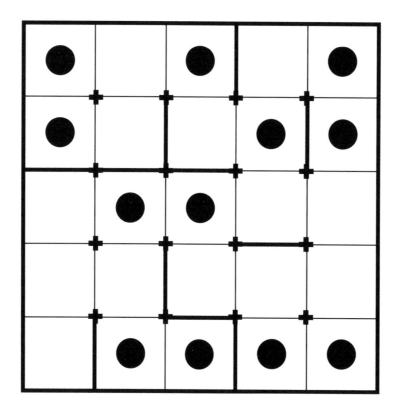

Shape Up

Every row and column in this grid originally contained one circle, one diamond, one square, one triangle and two blank squares, although not necessarily in that order.

Every symbol with a black arrow refers to the first of the four symbols encountered when moving in the direction of the arrow. Every symbol with a white arrow refers to the second of the four symbols encountered in the direction of the arrow.

Can you complete the original grid?

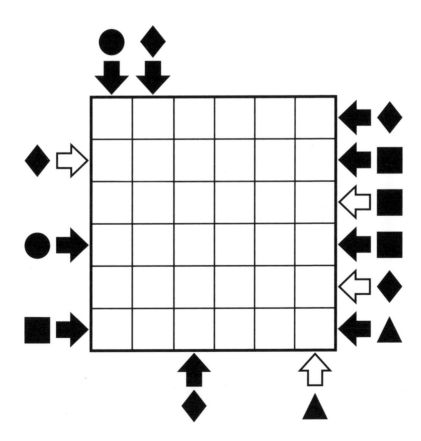

Total Concentration

The blank squares below should be filled with whole numbers between 1 and 40 inclusive, any of which may occur more than once, or not at all.

The numbers in every horizontal row add up to the totals on the right, as do the two long diagonal lines; whilst those in every vertical column add up to the totals along the bottom.

								115
33	11	37		23		22	2	164
21	18		31		13	13	39	167
32	35	25		24	11	21	19	203
6		29	31			26	18	186
38	24	39		18	22		23	213
	3	8	15		11	10	28	131
	9	20	29	22	19			161
13	12	35	24		39	29	31	221
188	145	202	213	208	152	150	188	179

Logi-6

Every row and column of this grid should contain one each of the letters A, B, C, D, E, and F. Each of the six shapes (marked by thicker lines) should also contain one each of the letters A, B, C, D, E, and F.

Can you complete the grid?

Hexagony

30

Can you place the hexagons into the grid, so that where any hexagon touches another along a straight line, the number in both triangles is the same? No rotation of any hexagon is allowed!

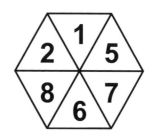

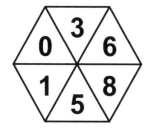

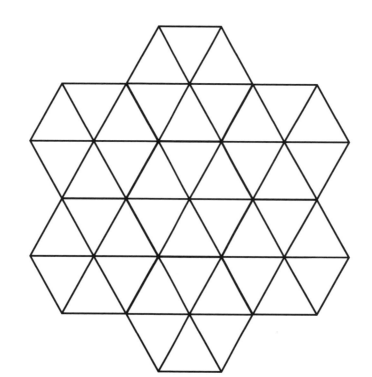

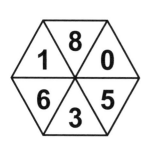

Ls in Place

Twelve L-shapes like the ones here need to be inserted
in the grid and each L has one hole in it.

There are three pieces of each of the four kinds shown here and
any piece may be turned or flipped over before being put in the
grid. No pieces of the same kind touch, even at a corner.

The pieces fit together so well that you cannot see any
spaces between them; only the holes show.

Can you tell where the Ls are?

Coin Collecting

In this puzzle, an amateur coin collector has been out with his metal detector, searching for booty. He didn't have time to dig up all the coins he found, so has made a grid map, showing their locations, in the hope that if he loses the map, at least no-one else will understand it…

Those squares containing numbers are empty, but where a number appears in a square, it indicates how many coins are located in the squares (up to a maximum of eight) surrounding the numbered one, touching it at any corner or side. There is only one coin in any individual square.

Place a circle into every square containing a coin.

						2		2	
	0	1			3	4		3	
	0		1					4	
				1					2
2							3	2	
		4				2	3		
2			0						
2			2	1		3	4	4	
							3		
	2	1	2			3		2	

Latin Square

The grid should be filled with numbers from 1 to 6, so that each number appears just once in every row and column.

The clues refer to the digit totals in the squares, eg A 1 2 3 = 6 means that the numbers in squares A1, A2 and A3 add up to 6.

	A	B	C	D	E	F
1						
2						
3						
4						
5						
6						

1 B 1 2 3 = 8

2 C 4 5 6 = 13

3 D 1 2 = 6

4 E 5 6 = 3

5 F 3 4 = 4

6 E F 1 = 6

7 E F 2 = 10

8 C D 3 = 10

9 D E 4 = 5

10 A B 5 = 4

11 A B 6 = 9

Simple as A, B, C?

Each of the small squares in the grid below contains either A, B or C. Each row, column, and diagonal line of six squares has exactly two of each letter.

Can you tell the letter in each square?

	1	2	3	4	5	6
1						
2						
3						
4						
5						
6						

Across

1 Any three consecutive squares contain three different letters.

2 The Bs are between the As.

3 The Cs are between the Bs.

5 One A is directly next to and left of a B. The other A is directly next to and right of a B.

Down

1 The As are higher than the Cs.

2 Each A is directly next to and above a B.

3 The Bs are higher than the Cs.

5 The As are between the Bs.

6 The Cs are adjacent to one another.

Zigzag

The object of this puzzle is to trace a single path from the top left corner to the bottom right corner of the grid, moving through all of the cells in either a horizontal, vertical or diagonal direction.

Every cell must be entered once only and your path should take you through the numbers in the sequence 1-2-3-4-5-6-1-2-3-4-5-6, etc.

Can you find the way?

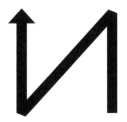

1	2	4	5	6	1
1	6	3	6	5	2
2	5	2	1	4	3
3	4	1	3	5	4
4	2	3	6	4	5
5	6	1	2	3	6

Battleships

Can you place the vessels into the diagram? Some parts of vessels or sea squares have already been filled in. A number to the right or below a row or column refers to the number of occupied squares in that row or column.

Any vessel may be positioned horizontally or vertically, but no part of a vessel touches part of any other vessel, either horizontally, vertically or diagonally.

Empty Area of Sea:

Aircraft Carrier:

Battleships:

Cruisers:

Submarines:

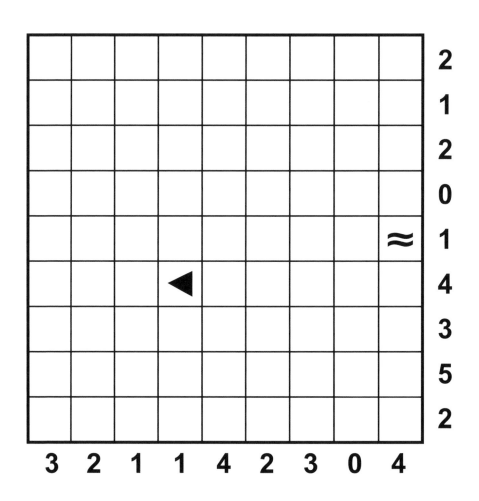

Slitherlink

Draw a single continuous loop, by connecting the dots.
No line may cross the path of another.

The figure inside each set of any four surrounding dots
indicates the total number of surrounding lines.

```
·   ·   ·   ·   ·   ·   ·   ·   ·
    0       2   2       2   2
·   ·   ·   ·   ·   ·   ·   ·   ·
    2       1           1   0
·   ·   ·   ·   ·   ·   ·   ·   ·
        0           2       1
·   ·   ·   ·   ·   ·   ·   ·   ·
  3       3       2       2   1
·   ·   ·   ·   ·   ·   ·   ·   ·
    2   2   2   1           0   3
·   ·   ·   ·   ·   ·   ·   ·   ·
  1               1   0   1
·   ·   ·   ·   ·   ·   ·   ·   ·
  1       1       2   2           0
·   ·   ·   ·   ·   ·   ·   ·   ·
  1           2       2       3
·   ·   ·   ·   ·   ·   ·   ·   ·
          1                   0
·   ·   ·   ·   ·   ·   ·   ·   ·
  1               1       2
·   ·   ·   ·   ·   ·   ·   ·   ·
    1   2   1               1   2
·   ·   ·   ·   ·   ·   ·   ·   ·
  1     3   2   3   3     3   2   2
·   ·   ·   ·   ·   ·   ·   ·   ·
```

Combiku

Each horizontal row and vertical column should contain different shapes and different numbers.

Every square will contain one number and one shape and no combination may be repeated anywhere else in the puzzle.

◇ 1   ○ 2   ☆ 3   ⬡ 4   ▢ 5

Mind Over Matter

Given that the letters are valued 1-26 according to their places in the alphabet, can you crack the mystery code to reveal the missing letter?

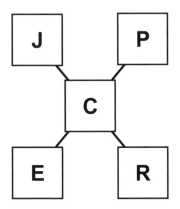

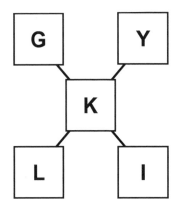

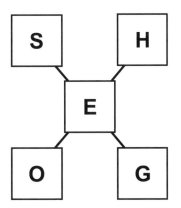

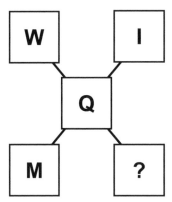

Tile Twister

Place the eight tiles into the puzzle grid so that all adjacent numbers on each tile match up. Tiles may be rotated through 360 degrees, but none may be flipped over.

2	4
3	1

1	3
2	1

2	2
4	3

2	4
1	3

1	4
4	2

1	4
2	4

1	2
2	2

1	3
4	4

It Doesn't Add Up

In the square below, change the positions of six numbers, one per horizontal row, vertical column and long diagonal line of six smaller squares, in such a way that the numbers in each row, column and long diagonal line total exactly 177.

Any number may appear more than once in a row, column or line.

53	29	14	36	42	21
14	31	34	50	26	16
34	36	32	29	27	22
11	47	58	3	9	27
33	27	2	33	26	33
10	25	40	56	41	35

Pyramid Plus

Every brick in this pyramid contains a number which is the sum of the two numbers below it, so that F=A+B, etc.

Just work out the missing numbers!

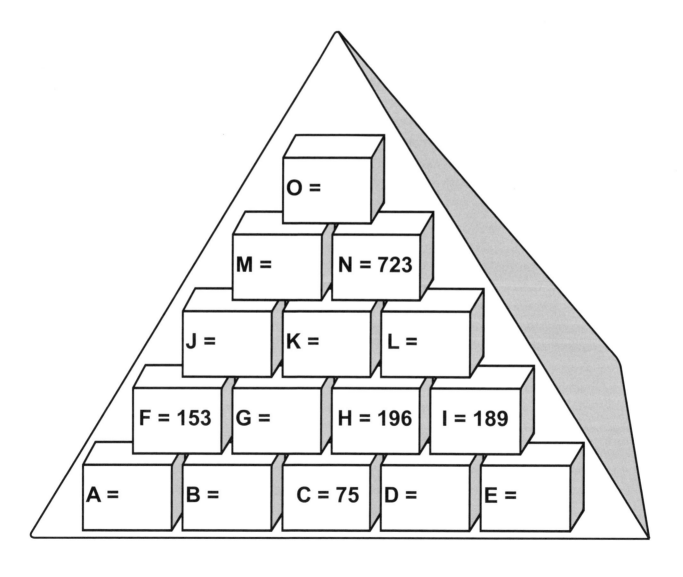

Treasure Hunt

The chart gives directions to a hidden treasure behind the black square in the grid. Move the indicated number of spaces north, south, east and west (eg 4N means move four squares north) stopping at every square once only to arrive there. At which square should you start?

N ⇧

1E	2S	2W	1W	1W
1S	1W	1W	1W	1S
1S	1E	■	1S	2N
2E	1S	2E	2N	2N
2E	1W	2E	2N	1W

W ⇦   ⇨ **E**

⇩ **S**

Futoshiki

Fill the grid so that every horizontal row and vertical column contains the numbers 1-5.

The "greater than" or "less than" signs indicate where a number is larger or smaller than that in the adjacent square.

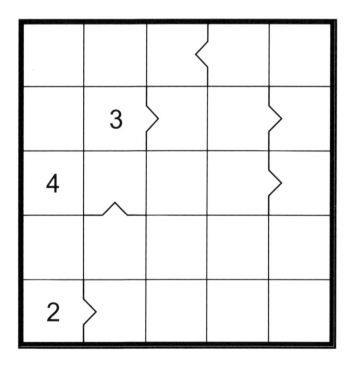

Eliminator

Every oval shape in this diagram contains a different letter of the alphabet from A to K inclusive. Use the clues to determine their locations. Reference in the clues to 'due' means in any location along the same horizontal or vertical line.

1   The A is next to and north of the D, which is next to and north of the G, which is due west of the C, which is due north of the I.

2   The B is due north of the F, which is next to and west of the E, which is further west than the I.

3   The J is further west and further south than the H, which is due east of the D.

4   The K is further south than the F.

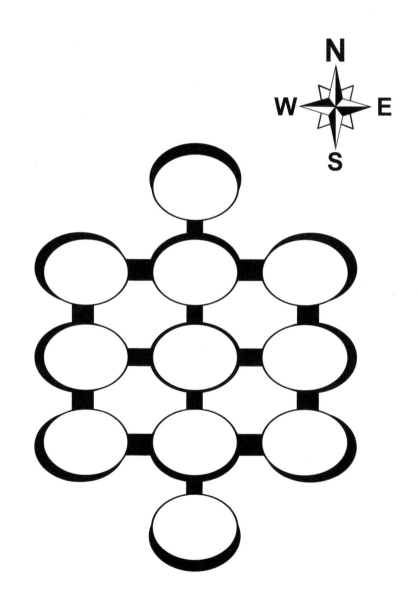

Sum Circle

Fill the three empty circles with the symbols +, − and x in some order, to make a sum which totals the central number. Each symbol must be used once and calculations are made in the direction of travel (clockwise).

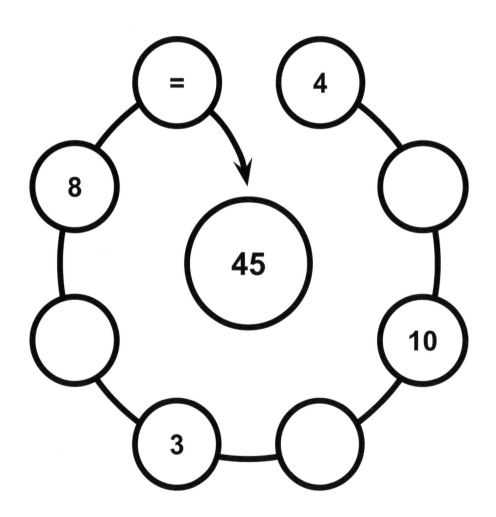

47

Spot Numbers

The numbers at the top and on the left side show the quantity of single-digit numbers (1-9) used in that row and column. The numbers at the bottom and on the right show the sum of the digits.

A number may appear more than once in a row or column, but no numbers are in squares that touch, even at a corner.

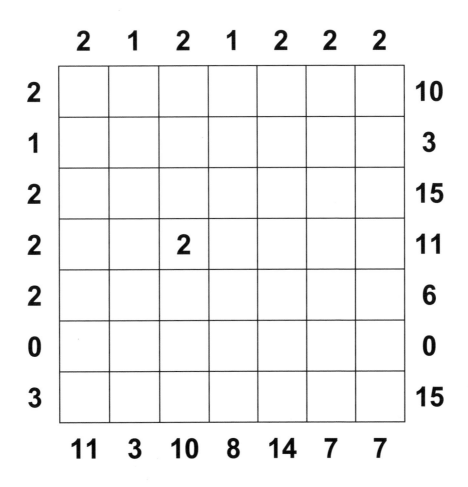

One to Nine

Using the numbers below, complete these six equations (three reading across and three reading downwards). Every number is used once.

1		2		3		4		5

		6		7		8		9	

	+		−		=	4
−	■	+	■	+		
	×		+		=	11
×	■	−	■	−		
	×		−		=	21
=		=		=		
16		10		7		

Domino Placement

A standard set of 28 dominoes has been laid out as shown.

Can you draw in the edges of them all?

The check-box is provided as an aid, and the domino already placed will help.

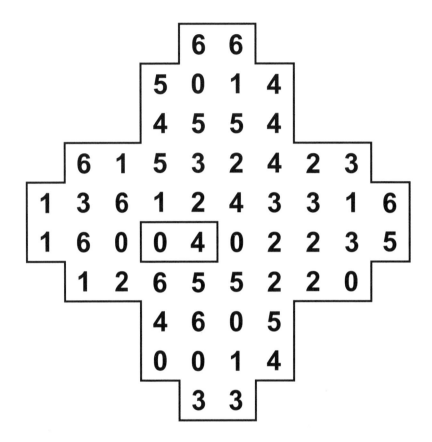

0-0	0-1	0-2	0-3	0-4	0-5	0-6	1-1	1-2	1-3	1-4	1-5	1-6	2-2
				✔									

2-3	2-4	2-5	2-6	3-3	3-4	3-5	3-6	4-4	4-5	4-6	5-5	5-6	6-6

Isolate

Draw walls to partition the grid into areas (some walls are already drawn in for you). Each area must contain two circles, area sizes must match those numbers shown above the grid and each '+' must be linked to at least two walls.

2, 3, 3, 4, 6, 7

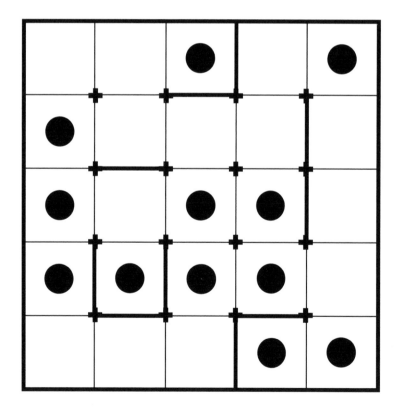

Shape Up

Every row and column in this grid originally contained one heart, one club, one diamond, one spade and two blank squares, although not necessarily in that order.

Every symbol with a black arrow refers to the first of the four symbols encountered when looking in the direction of the arrow. Every symbol with a white arrow refers to the second of the four symbols encountered in the direction of the arrow.

Can you complete the original grid?

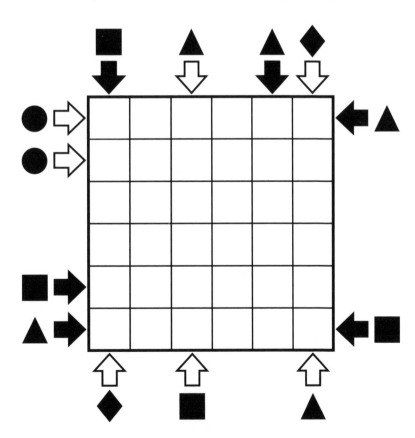

Total Concentration

The blank squares below should be filled with whole numbers between 1 and 40 inclusive, any of which may occur more than once, or not at all.

The numbers in every horizontal row add up to the totals on the right, as do the two long diagonal lines; whilst those in every vertical column add up to the totals along the bottom.

								127
5	32	26			6	24	14	152
13	30	25		29			13	182
	9	31	2	31	31	11		147
29	9		2	17		22	22	145
24			9		30	24	2	147
		15	1	25	39	35	30	175
21	3	33	38	17	16	37		173
14	25	29		32	13		26	188
124	150	177	141	193	180	204	140	203

Telling the Time

Draw in the missing hands on the final clock.

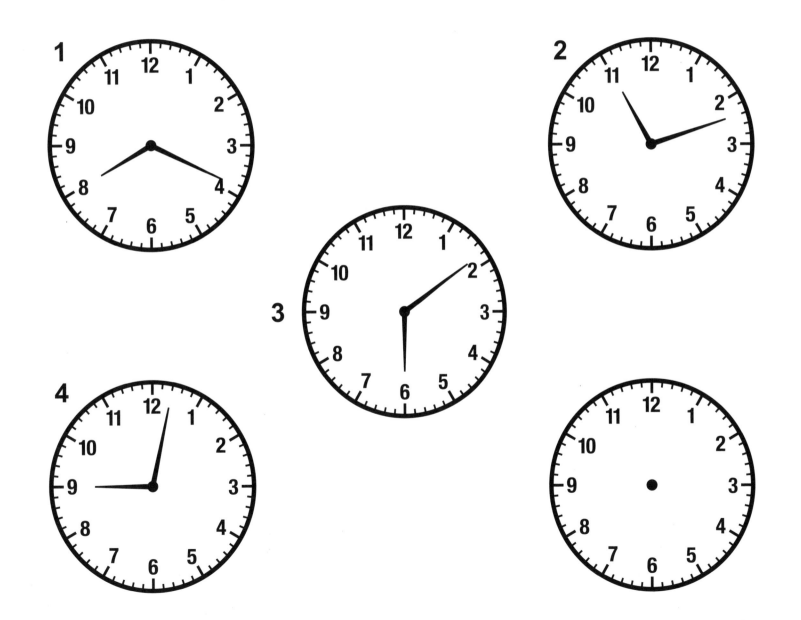

Hexagony

Can you place the hexagons into the grid, so that where any hexagon touches another along a straight line, the number in both triangles is the same? No rotation of any hexagon is allowed!

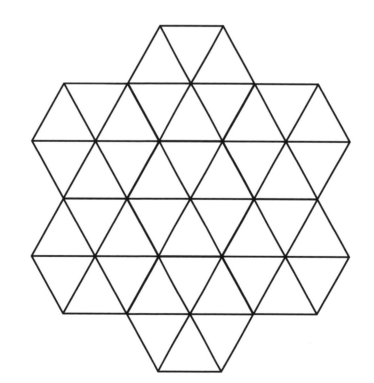

Ls in Place

Twelve L-shapes like the ones here need to be inserted in the grid and each L has one hole in it.

There are three pieces of each of the four kinds shown here and any piece may be turned or flipped over before being put in the grid. No pieces of the same kind touch, even at a corner.

The pieces fit together so well that you cannot see any spaces between them; only the holes show.

Can you tell where the Ls are?

Coin Collecting

In this puzzle, an amateur coin collector has been out with his metal detector, searching for booty. He didn't have time to dig up all the coins he found, so has made a grid map, showing their locations, in the hope that if he loses the map, at least no-one else will understand it…

Those squares containing numbers are empty, but where a number appears in a square, it indicates how many coins are located in the squares (up to a maximum of eight) surrounding the numbered one, touching it at any corner or side. There is only one coin in any individual square.

Place a circle into every square containing a coin.

0		1		1			1	2	1
0			2		1		0		1
				1	2		3		
1		3							
			1	3		3		1	
2		2							
			3		3	2			
2			6			3		1	
	0				4				

Latin Square

The grid should be filled with numbers from 1 to 6, so that each number appears just once in every row and column.

The clues refer to the digit totals in the squares, eg A 1 2 3 = 6 means that the numbers in squares A1, A2 and A3 add up to 6.

	A	B	C	D	E	F
1						
2						
3						
4						
5						
6						

1 A B 4 = 8

2 E F 5 = 9

3 C D 6 = 9

4 A 5 6 = 8

5 B 1 2 = 11

6 C 3 4 = 3

7 D 2 3 4 = 7

8 E 3 4 = 11

9 F 3 4 = 8

10 D E F 1 = 9

11 E F 2 = 7

Simple as A, B, C?

Each of the small squares in the grid below contains either A, B or C. Each row, column, and diagonal line of six squares has exactly two of each letter.

Can you tell the letter in each square?

	1	2	3	4	5	6
1						
2						
3						
4						
5						
6						

Across

1 The As are between the Cs.

2 The Cs are between the Bs.

3 The Bs are in adjacent squares.

4 The Cs are further right than the As.

5 The Bs are further right than the As.

6 Each B is directly next to and left of a C.

Down

1 No two squares containing the same letter are adjacent.

2 The Cs are between the Bs.

6 The Bs are lower than the Cs.

Zigzag

The object of this puzzle is to trace a single path from the top left corner to the bottom right corner of the grid, moving through all of the cells in either a horizontal, vertical or diagonal direction.

Every cell must be entered once only and your path should take you through the numbers in the sequence 1-2-3-4-5-6-1-2-3-4-5-6, etc.

Can you find the way?

1	6	5	6	2	3
2	4	1	1	5	4
3	2	1	6	5	4
1	3	4	2	3	3
2	6	5	4	5	2
3	4	5	6	1	6

Battleships

Can you place the vessels into the diagram? Some parts of vessels or sea squares have already been filled in. A number to the right or below a row or column refers to the number of occupied squares in that row or column.

Any vessel may be positioned horizontally or vertically, but no part of a vessel touches part of any other vessel, either horizontally, vertically or diagonally.

Empty Area of Sea:

Aircraft Carrier:

Battleships:

Cruisers:

Submarines:

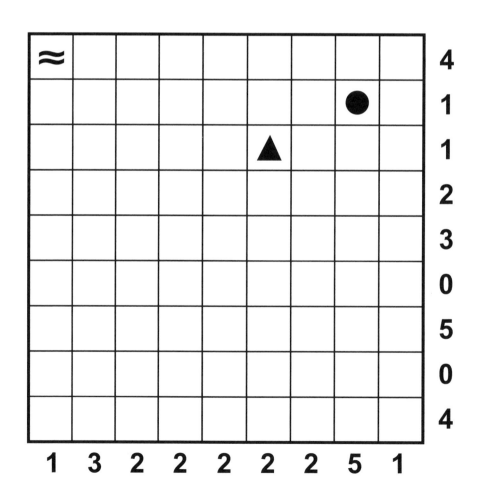

Slitherlink

Draw a single continuous loop, by connecting the dots.
No line may cross the path of another.

The figure inside each set of any four surrounding dots
indicates the total number of surrounding lines.

```
. . . . . . . . . . .
  0       3   1
. . . . . . . . . .
  1     1 1 0       0 2
. . . . . . . . . . .
              0       0 2
. . . . . . . . . . .
  1                   1
. . . . . . . . . . .
  1 1       1       0 2
. . . . . . . . . . .
1     1 1     1     0
. . . . . . . . . . .
    0     3 1     1 3
. . . . . . . . . . .
1     1       0
. . . . . . . . . . .
  2 0               3 2
. . . . . . . . . . .
  0     3     0 1     2
. . . . . . . . . . .
2 0 2         3 2     2
. . . . . . . . . . .
                  3
. . . . . . . . . . .
```

Combiku

Each horizontal row and vertical column should contain different shapes and different numbers.

Every square will contain one number and one shape and no combination may be repeated anywhere else in the puzzle.

◇ ○ ☆ ⬡ ▢
1   2   3   4   5

Mind Over Matter

★★

Given that the letters are valued 1-26 according to their places in the alphabet, can you crack the mystery code to reveal the missing letter?

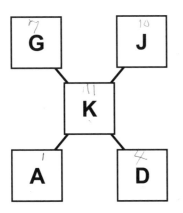

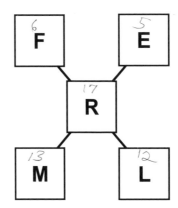

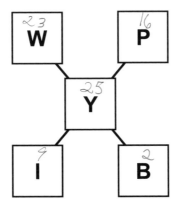

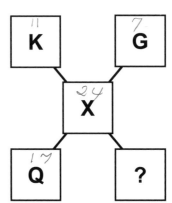

64

★★

Tile Twister

Place the eight tiles into the puzzle grid so that all adjacent numbers on each tile match up. Tiles may be rotated through 360 degrees, but none may be flipped over.

3	4
1	3

1	1
3	2

1	4
3	2

1	2
3	4

1	3
3	2

1	3
1	2

		4	3		
		3	2		

4	1
3	3

3	2
4	4

It Doesn't Add Up

In the square below, change the positions of six numbers, one per horizontal row, vertical column and long diagonal line of six smaller squares, in such a way that the numbers in each row, column and long diagonal line total exactly 163.

Any number may appear more than once in a row, column or line.

32	16	21	25	38	32
34	36	29	15	28	30
40	32	27	30	12	31
20	48	28	33	17	28
15	21	32	33	32	27
33	19	27	36	9	12

Pyramid Plus

Every brick in this pyramid contains a number which is the sum of the two numbers below it, so that F=A+B, etc.

Just work out the missing numbers!

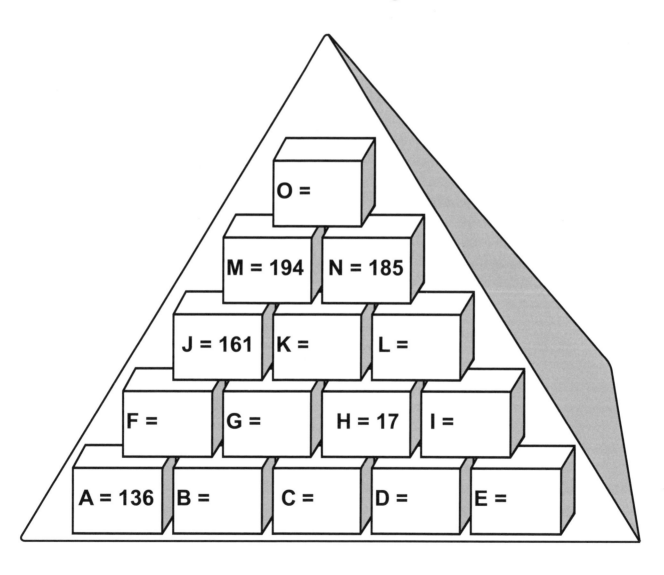

O =

M = 194   N = 185

J = 161   K =   L =

F =   G =   H = 17   I =

A = 136   B =   C =   D =   E =

Treasure Hunt

The chart gives directions to a hidden treasure behind the black square in the grid. Move the indicated number of spaces north, south, east and west (eg 4N means move four squares north) stopping at every square once only to arrive there. At which square should you start?

N ⇧

1S	1S	1W	3W	1W
3S	1S	1N	1S	1W
2E	3E	■	3W	1S
1E	1E	1S	3W	2N
1E	3E	3N	1N	1W

W ⇦   ⇨ **E**

⇩ **S**

Futoshiki

Fill the grid so that every horizontal row and vertical
column contains the numbers 1-5.

The "greater than" or "less than" signs indicate where a number
is larger or smaller than that in the adjacent square.

	2			<
1				
4			>	
	5		<	
			2	4

Eliminator

Every oval shape in this diagram contains a different letter of the alphabet from A to K inclusive. Use the clues to determine their locations. Reference in the clues to 'due' means in any location along the same horizontal or vertical line.

1 The E is next to and south of the G, which is next to and east of the J.

2 The F is due south of both the B and the K.

3 The J is further south than the C, which is next to and east of the H, which is next to and south of the A.

4 The K is next to and east of the I, which is next to and south of the D, which is further east than the A.

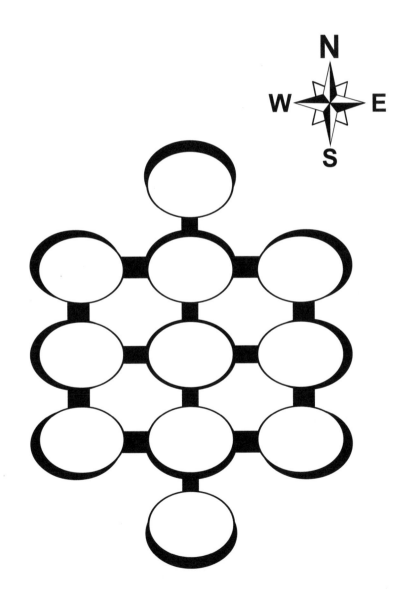

Sum Circle

Fill the three empty circles with the symbols +, − and x in some order, to make a sum which totals the central number. Each symbol must be used once and calculations are made in the direction of travel (clockwise).

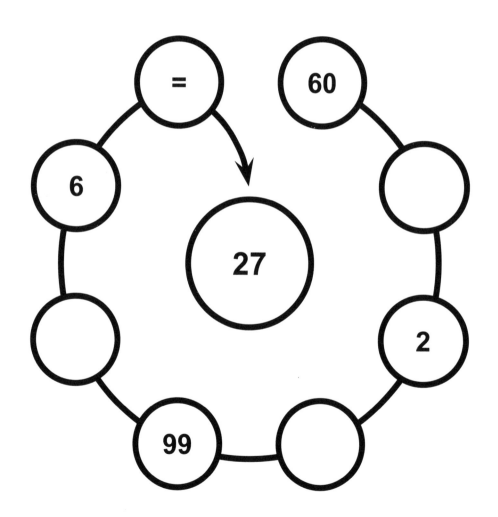

Spot Numbers

The numbers at the top and on the left side show the quantity of single-digit numbers (1-9) used in that row and column. The numbers at the bottom and on the right show the sum of the digits.

A number may appear more than once in a row or column, but no numbers are in squares that touch, even at a corner.

	3	1	2	2	1	1	2	
2								6
1								4
2								11
0								0
3			3					21
1								8
3								25
	19	9	12	6	8	4	17	

One to Nine

Using the numbers below, complete these six equations (three reading across and three reading downwards). Every number is used once.

1   **2**   **3**   **4**   **5**

6   **7**   **8**   **9**

	x		x		=	12
x	■	+	■	−		
	−		x		=	2
+	■	+	■	+		
	−		x		=	32
=		=		=		
37		12		9		

73

Domino Placement

A standard set of 28 dominoes has been laid out as shown.

Can you draw in the edges of them all?

The check-box is provided as an aid, and the domino already placed will help.

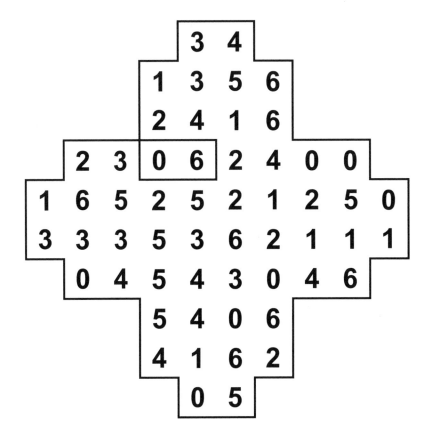

0-0	0-1	0-2	0-3	0-4	0-5	0-6	1-1	1-2	1-3	1-4	1-5	1-6	2-2
						✔							

2-3	2-4	2-5	2-6	3-3	3-4	3-5	3-6	4-4	4-5	4-6	5-5	5-6	6-6

Isolate

Draw walls to partition the grid into areas (some walls are already drawn in for you). Each area must contain two circles, area sizes must match those numbers shown above the grid and each '+' must be linked to at least two walls.

2, 3, 4, 4, 5, 7

Shape Up

Every row and column in this grid originally contained one circle, one diamond, one square, one triangle and two blank squares, although not necessarily in that order.

Every symbol with a black arrow refers to the first of the four symbols encountered when moving in the direction of the arrow. Every symbol with a white arrow refers to the second of the four symbols encountered in the direction of the arrow.

Can you complete the original grid?

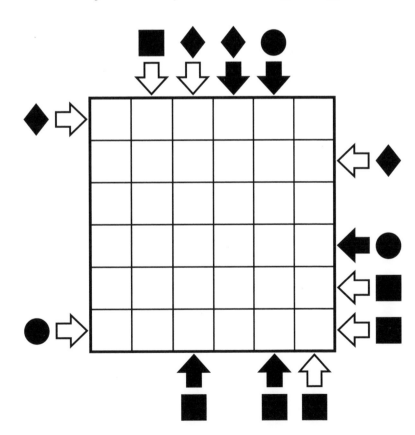

Total Concentration

The blank squares below should be filled with whole numbers between 1 and 40 inclusive, any of which may occur more than once, or not at all.

The numbers in every horizontal row add up to the totals on the right, as do the two long diagonal lines; whilst those in every vertical column add up to the totals along the bottom.

								129
	17	40	25	15		30		187
23	6	13	26		29	38	11	167
32		27	22	12			6	128
	22		10	18	25		39	214
12	29	8		36	28	31		184
1	9	9	27	15	29	12		115
39	24	24	21			3	14	175
2	37	17		31	23	36	23	182
164	161	171	161	168	183	196	148	158

Logi-6

Every row and column of this grid should contain one each of the letters A, B, C, D, E, and F. Each of the six shapes (marked by thicker lines) should also contain one each of the letters A, B, C, D, E, and F.

Can you complete the grid?

			B		A
D				C	
E					
F					

Hexagony

Can you place the hexagons into the grid, so that where any hexagon touches another along a straight line, the number in both triangles is the same? No rotation of any hexagon is allowed!

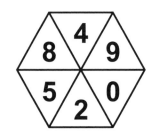

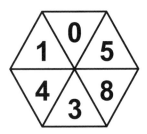
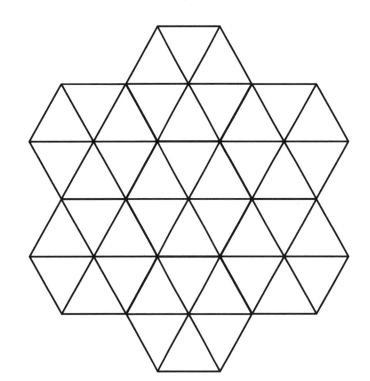

Ls in Place

Twelve L-shapes like the ones here need to be inserted
in the grid and each L has one hole in it.

There are three pieces of each of the four kinds shown here and
any piece may be turned or flipped over before being put in the
grid. No pieces of the same kind touch, even at a corner.

The pieces fit together so well that you cannot see any
spaces between them; only the holes show.

Can you tell where the Ls are?

Coin Collecting

In this puzzle, an amateur coin collector has been out with his metal detector, searching for booty. He didn't have time to dig up all the coins he found, so has made a grid map, showing their locations, in the hope that if he loses the map, at least no-one else will understand it…

Those squares containing numbers are empty, but where a number appears in a square, it indicates how many coins are located in the squares (up to a maximum of eight) surrounding the numbered one, touching it at any corner or side. There is only one coin in any individual square.

Place a circle into every square containing a coin.

	2			0		0		2	
2				2	1		2		
					2			3	
0		2							2
		1		2		1	3		
							3	4	3
	2	1			2				
			0			3	3		
0						3	3		2
			2				2		

Latin Square

The grid should be filled with numbers from 1 to 6, so that each number appears just once in every row and column.

The clues refer to the digit totals in the squares, eg A 1 2 3 = 6 means that the numbers in squares A1, A2 and A3 add up to 6.

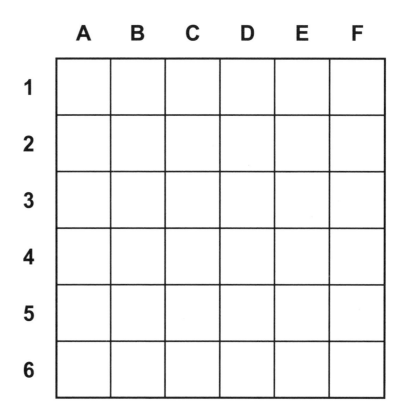

1 D E 1 = 4

2 C D 2 = 8

3 A B C 3 = 9

4 D E 4 = 8

5 E F 5 = 7

6 B C 6 = 5

7 A 4 5 6 = 12

8 B 4 5 = 4

9 C 4 5 = 11

10 D 5 6 = 10

11 E 2 3 = 5

Simple as A, B, C?

Each of the small squares in the grid below contains either A, B or C. Each row, column, and diagonal line of six squares has exactly two of each letter.

Can you tell the letter in each square?

Across

1 The Cs are further left than the As.

2 The Bs are further left than the Cs.

6 The Cs are between the Bs.

Down

1 The Bs are between the As.

2 Each B is directly next to and above an A.

3 The As are higher than the Cs.

4 The As are higher than the Cs.

5 The Bs are between the Cs.

6 The As are between the Bs.

Zigzag

The object of this puzzle is to trace a single path from the top left corner to the bottom right corner of the grid, moving through all of the cells in either a horizontal, vertical or diagonal direction.

Every cell must be entered once only and your path should take you through the numbers in the sequence 1-2-3-4-5-6-1-2-3-4-5-6, etc.

Can you find the way?

1	2	6	1	6	5
4	5	3	1	2	4
3	6	5	4	2	3
2	1	4	3	6	2
1	2	4	5	3	1
6	5	3	4	5	6

Battleships

Can you place the vessels into the diagram? Some parts of vessels or sea squares have already been filled in. A number to the right or below a row or column refers to the number of occupied squares in that row or column.

Any vessel may be positioned horizontally or vertically, but no part of a vessel touches part of any other vessel, either horizontally, vertically or diagonally.

Empty Area of Sea:

Aircraft Carrier:

Battleships:

Cruisers:

Submarines:

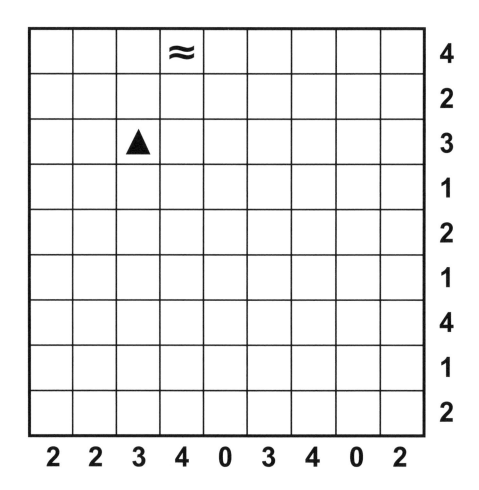

Slitherlink

Draw a single continuous loop, by connecting the dots.
No line may cross the path of another.

The figure inside each set of any four surrounding dots
indicates the total number of surrounding lines.

```
.   .   .   .   .   .   .   .   .   .   .
          3           1
.   .   .   .   .   .   .   .   .   .   .
  1   0   2   0               3       1
.   .   .   .   .   .   .   .   .   .   .
              1       1   2   1   1
.   .   .   .   .   .   .   .   .   .   .
      2           3   1       3
.   .   .   .   .   .   .   .   .   .   .
  2   2           1       1   3
.   .   .   .   .   .   .   .   .   .   .
  2   2   2           0           2
.   .   .   .   .   .   .   .   .   .   .
      2   1           1   3       3
.   .   .   .   .   .   .   .   .   .   .
          1               3
.   .   .   .   .   .   .   .   .   .   .
      2   1   3   1       2   2       1
.   .   .   .   .   .   .   .   .   .   .
  3       1       3           3
.   .   .   .   .   .   .   .   .   .   .
      1   2                   2       1
.   .   .   .   .   .   .   .   .   .   .
  3               3           0
.   .   .   .   .   .   .   .   .   .   .
```

Combiku

Each horizontal row and vertical column should contain different shapes and different numbers.

Every square will contain one number and one shape and no combination may be repeated anywhere else in the puzzle.

◇ 1   ○ 2   ☆ 3   ⬡ 4   ☐ 5

◇				
③	☐			
		4	◇	5
	◇		⬡2	
⬡	2	☆3		

Mind Over Matter

★★

Given that the letters are valued 1-26 according to their places in the alphabet, can you crack the mystery code to reveal the missing letter?

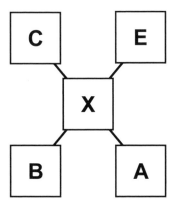

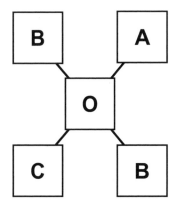

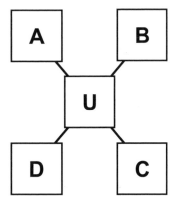

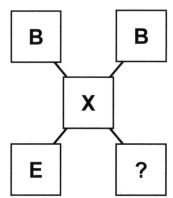

88

★★

Tile Twister

Place the eight tiles into the puzzle grid so that all adjacent numbers on each tile match up. Tiles may be rotated through 360 degrees, but none may be flipped over.

3	4
1	1

1	3
1	2

4	1
1	3

4	2
2	1

2	4
1	4

2	1
1	4

1	2
1	1

2	4
1	3

				1	4
				4	2

It Doesn't Add Up

In the square below, change the positions of six numbers, one per horizontal row, vertical column and long diagonal line of six smaller squares, in such a way that the numbers in each row, column and long diagonal line total exactly 214.

Any number may appear more than once in a row, column or line.

44	18	30	26	52	42
19	35	18	25	39	37
21	50	35	51	25	23
57	43	39	59	17	39
18	27	44	51	39	29
14	32	42	42	60	42

Pyramid Plus

Every brick in this pyramid contains a number which is the sum of the two numbers below it, so that F=A+B, etc.

Just work out the missing numbers!

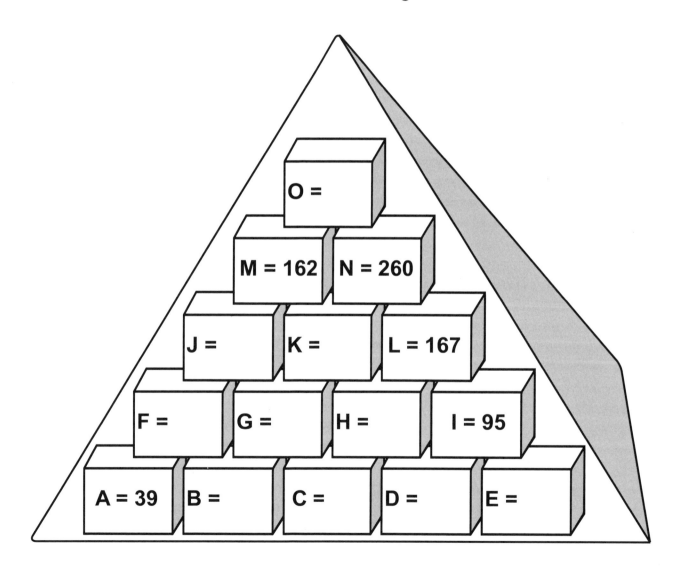

Treasure Hunt

The chart gives directions to a hidden treasure behind the black square in the grid. Move the indicated number of spaces north, south, east and west (eg 4N means move four squares north) stopping at every square once only to arrive there. At which square should you start?

N
⇧

2E	1S	1W	2S	1W
3E	3E	3S	1W	3S
2N	1S	■	2S	2N
2N	1E	2E	3W	1W
2N	2N	2N	2W	2N

W ⇦   ⇨ **E**

⇩
S

Futoshiki

Fill the grid so that every horizontal row and vertical column contains the numbers 1-5.

The "greater than" or "less than" signs indicate where a number is larger or smaller than that in the adjacent square.

	2		5	
			2	
		4		2

Figure It Out

What number should replace the question mark?

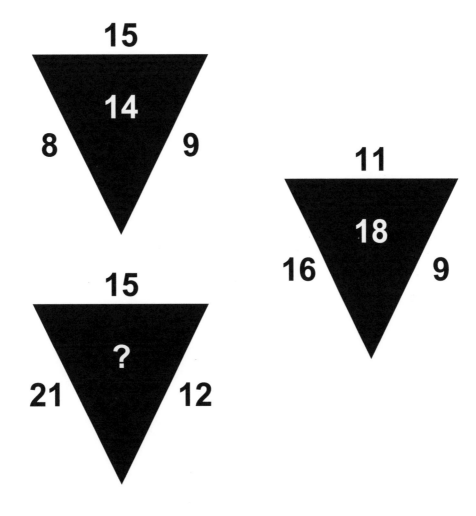

Symbol Sums

Each symbol stands for a different number. In order to reach the correct total at the end of each row and column, what is the value of the circle, cross, pentagon, square and star?

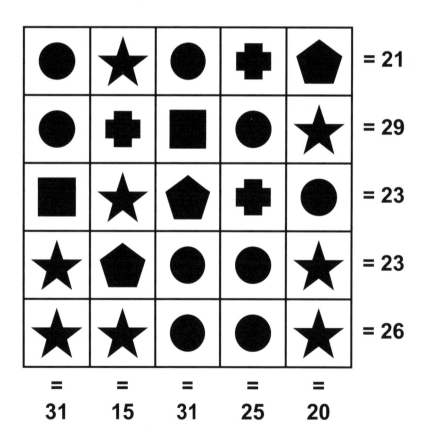

Missing Number

In the grid below, what number should replace the question mark?

183	120	68	69	86	81	153
171	109	58	60	78	74	147
159	98	48	51	70	67	141
147	87	38	42	62	60	135
135	76	28	33	54	53	129
123	65	18	24	?	46	123
111	54	8	15	38	39	117

One to Nine

Using the numbers below, complete these six equations (three reading across and three reading downwards). Every number is used once.

| 1 | | 2 | | 3 | | 4 | | 5 |

| | 6 | | 7 | | 8 | | 9 |

	x		–		=	19
–		x		+		
	x		x		=	18
x		+		–		
	+		x		=	26
=		=		=		
15		50		10		

Domino Placement

A standard set of 28 dominoes has been laid out as shown.

Can you draw in the edges of them all?

The check-box is provided as an aid, and the domino already placed will help.

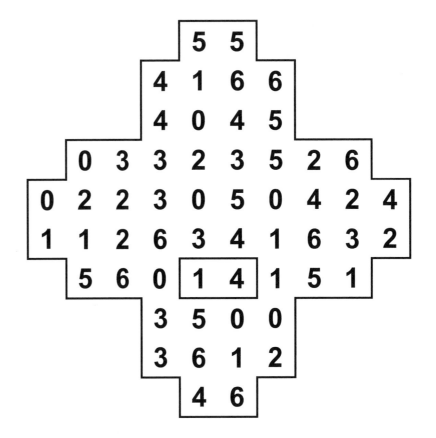

0-0	0-1	0-2	0-3	0-4	0-5	0-6	1-1	1-2	1-3	1-4	1-5	1-6	2-2
										✓			

2-3	2-4	2-5	2-6	3-3	3-4	3-5	3-6	4-4	4-5	4-6	5-5	5-6	6-6

Isolate

Draw walls to partition the grid into areas (some walls are already drawn in for you). Each area must contain two circles, area sizes must match those numbers shown above the grid and each '+' must be linked to at least two walls.

3, 3, 5, 7, 7

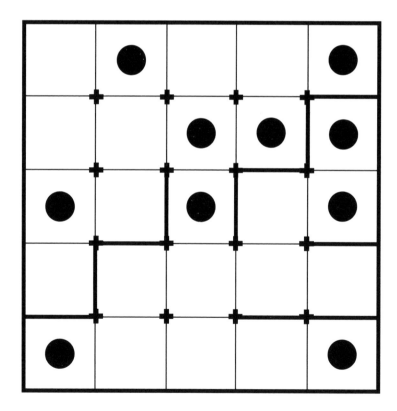

Shape Up

Every row and column in this grid originally contained one heart, one club, one diamond, one spade and two blank squares, although not necessarily in that order.

Every symbol with a black arrow refers to the first of the four symbols encountered when looking in the direction of the arrow. Every symbol with a white arrow refers to the second of the four symbols encountered in the direction of the arrow.

Can you complete the original grid?

Total Concentration

The blank squares below should be filled with whole numbers between 1 and 30 inclusive, any of which may occur more than once, or not at all.

The numbers in every horizontal row add up to the totals on the right, as do the two long diagonal lines; whilst those in every vertical column add up to the totals along the bottom.

							120
16	17			9	11	20	100
10		15	7	16		13	99
	5	28		1		26	127
	12	14	22	20	13		108
2	15		17		18		115
25	16	12	20		5	4	106
10	14	26	4		19	13	104
87	93	145	104	96	109	125	106

Telling the Time

Draw in the missing hands on the final clock.

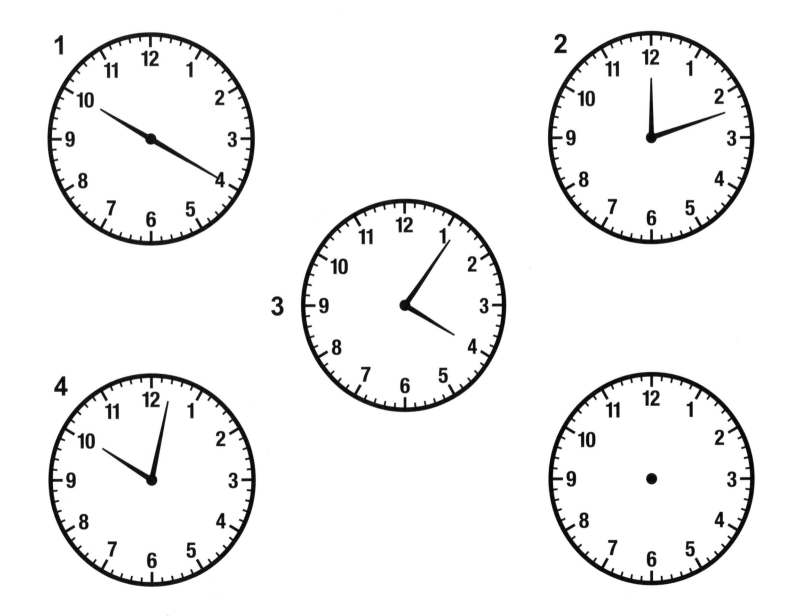

Hexagony

Can you place the hexagons into the grid, so that where any hexagon touches another along a straight line, the number in both triangles is the same? No rotation of any hexagon is allowed!

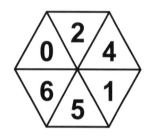

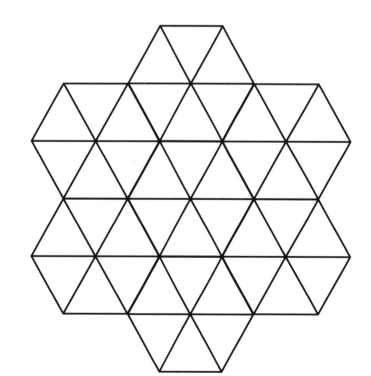

Ls in Place

Twelve L-shapes like the ones here need to be inserted in the grid and each L has one hole in it.

There are three pieces of each of the four kinds shown here and any piece may be turned or flipped over before being put in the grid. No pieces of the same kind touch, even at a corner.

The pieces fit together so well that you cannot see any spaces between them; only the holes show.

Can you tell where the Ls are?

Coin Collecting

In this puzzle, an amateur coin collector has been out with his metal detector, searching for booty. He didn't have time to dig up all the coins he found, so has made a grid map, showing their locations, in the hope that if he loses the map, at least no-one else will understand it…

Those squares containing numbers are empty, but where a number appears in a square, it indicates how many coins are located in the squares (up to a maximum of eight) surrounding the numbered one, touching it at any corner or side. There is only one coin in any individual square.

Place a circle into every square containing a coin.

	2				2			2	
1				2		1			
2	2		2				3		2
1				2	2				
						2	3		2
		2	2	2			3		
	2		1						2
		0			1		3	3	
2			3			1	2		
	1							1	

Latin Square

The grid should be filled with numbers from 1 to 6, so that each number appears just once in every row and column.

The clues refer to the digit totals in the squares, eg A 1 2 3 = 6 means that the numbers in squares A1, A2 and A3 add up to 6.

	A	B	C	D	E	F
1						
2						
3						
4						
5						
6						

1 C D 5 = 6

2 D E 6 = 6

3 A 1 2 = 3

4 B 1 2 = 9

5 C 1 2 3 = 8

6 D 2 3 = 9

7 E 3 4 = 11

8 F 3 4 5 = 13

9 D E 1 = 8

10 E F 2 = 5

11 A B 3 = 10

Simple as A, B, C?

Each of the small squares in the grid below contains either A, B or C. Each row, column, and diagonal line of six squares has exactly two of each letter.

Can you tell the letter in each square?

	1	2	3	4	5	6
1						
2						
3						
4						
5						
6						

Across

2 The Cs are between the As

4 The As are between the Cs

5 No two letters the same are directly next to each other

Down

2 The Cs are next to each other

3 The Bs are between the Cs

4 The Cs are between the As

5 The Cs are lower than the As

6 The Bs are next to each other

Zigzag

The object of this puzzle is to trace a single path from the top left corner to the bottom right corner of the grid, moving through all of the cells in either a horizontal, vertical or diagonal direction.

Every cell must be entered once only and your path should take you through the numbers in the sequence 1-2-3-4-1-2-3-4, etc.

Can you find the way?

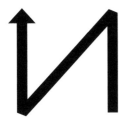

1	4	1	1	2	1	4	3
3	2	4	2	1	3	2	4
1	3	3	4	2	3	1	4
2	4	2	4	4	2	3	1
3	1	3	1	1	2	2	3
2	3	4	4	1	4	3	4
4	2	2	2	3	1	1	2
3	1	1	4	3	2	3	4

Battleships

Can you place the vessels into the diagram? Some parts of vessels or sea squares have already been filled in. A number to the right or below a row or column refers to the number of occupied squares in that row or column.

Any vessel may be positioned horizontally or vertically, but no part of a vessel touches part of any other vessel, either horizontally, vertically or diagonally.

Empty Area of Sea:

Aircraft Carrier:

Battleships:

Cruisers:

Submarines:

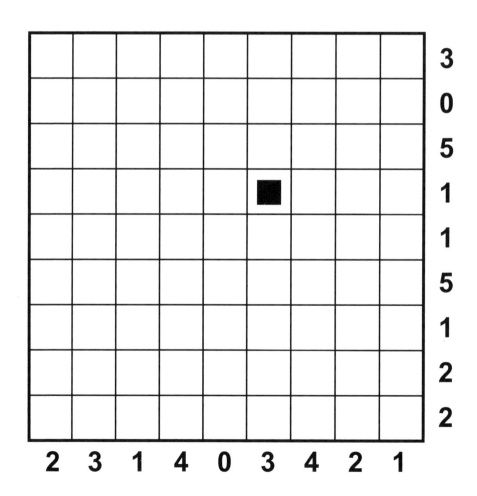

Slitherlink

Draw a single continuous loop, by connecting the dots.
No line may cross the path of another.

The figure inside each set of any four surrounding dots
indicates the total number of surrounding lines.

```
·   ·   ·   ·   ·   ·   ·   ·   ·   ·   ·
    0           1       1   1   2
·   ·   ·   ·   ·   ·   ·   ·   ·   ·   ·
                        0   1
·   ·   ·   ·   ·   ·   ·   ·   ·   ·   ·
        2   1       1           2   2
·   ·   ·   ·   ·   ·   ·   ·   ·   ·   ·
    0           1       0
·   ·   ·   ·   ·   ·   ·   ·   ·   ·   ·
            2   0       0   2   2   3
·   ·   ·   ·   ·   ·   ·   ·   ·   ·   ·
  1         2   2               3
·   ·   ·   ·   ·   ·   ·   ·   ·   ·   ·
  1         2           0       1
·   ·   ·   ·   ·   ·   ·   ·   ·   ·   ·
    0   0                   1   3
·   ·   ·   ·   ·   ·   ·   ·   ·   ·   ·
    1                           0
·   ·   ·   ·   ·   ·   ·   ·   ·   ·   ·
        0   1   0
·   ·   ·   ·   ·   ·   ·   ·   ·   ·   ·
  1             0       1   2
·   ·   ·   ·   ·   ·   ·   ·   ·   ·   ·
    1   2       2   1       3
·   ·   ·   ·   ·   ·   ·   ·   ·   ·   ·
```

Combiku

Each horizontal row and vertical column should contain different shapes and different numbers.

Every square will contain one number and one shape and no combination may be repeated anywhere else in the puzzle.

◇ ○ ☆ ⬡ ▢
1   **2**   **3**   **4**   **5**

		3		
▢1		◇	○	
	◇4		▢5	⬡
	2		1	
	1			

Mind Over Matter

★★★

Given that the letters are valued 1-26 according to their places in the alphabet, can you crack the mystery code to reveal the missing letter?

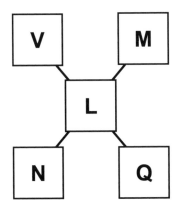

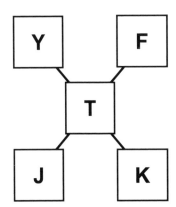

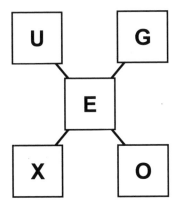

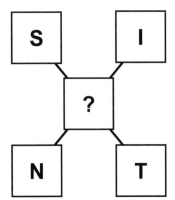

Tile Twister

Place the eight tiles into the puzzle grid so that all adjacent numbers on each tile match up. Tiles may be rotated through 360 degrees, but none may be flipped over.

4	4
1	1

2	4
2	1

3	1
2	3

4	1
2	3

2	2
4	3

4	3
4	3

1	3
4	1

4	2
3	1

Grid (with pre-placed values):

				2	1
				3	3

It Doesn't Add Up

In the square below, change the positions of six numbers, one per horizontal row, vertical column and long diagonal line of six smaller squares, in such a way that the numbers in each row, column and long diagonal line total exactly 264.

Any number may appear more than once in a row, column or line.

37	52	56	77	51	37
10	66	39	28	20	42
54	20	38	74	61	35
35	19	84	12	46	77
32	30	57	26	68	45
37	69	36	65	12	37

Pyramid Plus

Every brick in this pyramid contains a number which is the sum of the two numbers below it, so that F=A+B, etc.

Just work out the missing numbers!

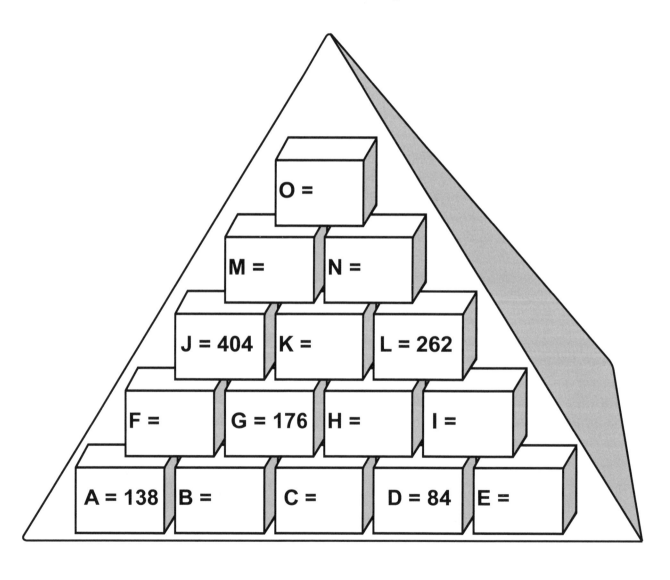

O =

M =   N =

J = 404   K =   L = 262

F =   G = 176   H =   I =

A = 138   B =   C =   D = 84   E =

Treasure Hunt

The chart gives directions to a hidden treasure behind the black square in the grid. Move the indicated number of spaces north, south, east and west (eg 4N means move four squares north) stopping at every square once only to arrive there. At which square should you start?

N
⇧

2E	2S	2E	3S	1W
1N	1E	2E	2W	3S
3E	3E	■	1N	2W
1N	3N	1W	1E	2W
3N	2E	1W	3W	2W

W ⇦   ⇨ **E**

⇩
S

Futoshiki

Fill the grid so that every horizontal row and vertical column contains the numbers 1-5.

The "greater than" or "less than" signs indicate where a number is larger or smaller than that in the adjacent square.

		1		5
			3	
	1	4		
	5			

Eliminator

★★★

Every oval shape in this diagram contains a different letter of the alphabet from A to K inclusive. Use the clues to determine their locations. Reference in the clues to 'due' means in any location along the same horizontal or vertical line.

1   The A is due west of the H, which is next to and north of the F, which is next to and east of the E.

2   The C is due south of the D, which is next to and west of the K, which is next to and south of the B, which is further north than the G.

3   The J is due south of the I, which is next to and west of the H.

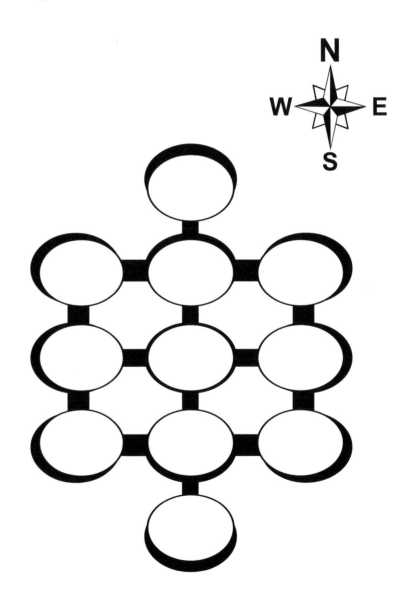

Sum Circle

Fill the three empty circles with the symbols +, − and x in some order, to make a sum which totals the central number. Each symbol must be used once and calculations are made in the direction of travel (clockwise).

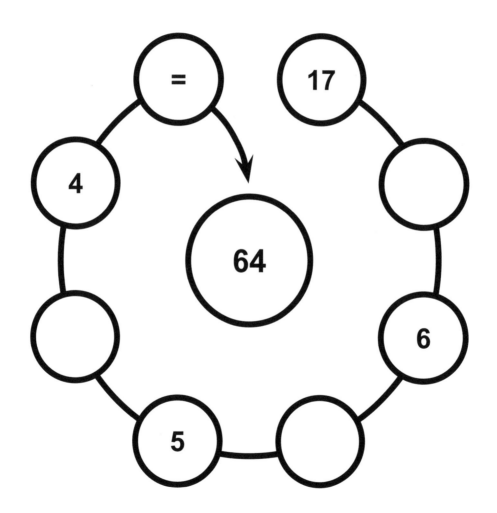

Spot Numbers

The numbers at the top and on the left side show the quantity of single-digit numbers (1-9) used in that row and column. The numbers at the bottom and on the right show the sum of the digits.

A number may appear more than once in a row or column, but no numbers are in squares that touch, even at a corner.

	2	1	2	1	3	0	3	
2								18
2							1	5
2								12
2								10
1								7
2								9
1								8
	15	2	8	8	22	0	14	

One to Nine

Using the numbers below, complete these six equations (three reading across and three reading downwards). Every number is used once.

1   2   3   4   5

6   7   8   9

	+		+		=	9
+		−		+		
	+		x		=	42
x		x		+		
	x		+		=	57
=		=		=		
72		6		17		

Domino Placement

A standard set of 28 dominoes has been laid out as shown.

Can you draw in the edges of them all?

The check-box is provided as an aid, and the domino already placed will help.

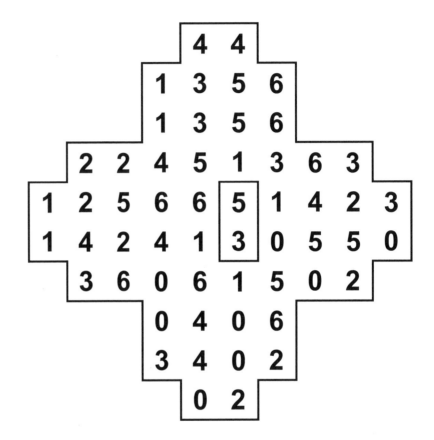

0-0	0-1	0-2	0-3	0-4	0-5	0-6	1-1	1-2	1-3	1-4	1-5	1-6	2-2

2-3	2-4	2-5	2-6	3-3	3-4	3-5	3-6	4-4	4-5	4-6	5-5	5-6	6-6
						✔							

Isolate

Draw walls to partition the grid into areas (some walls are already drawn in for you). Each area must contain two circles, area sizes must match those numbers shown above the grid and each '+' must be linked to at least two walls.

3, 4, 5, 6, 7

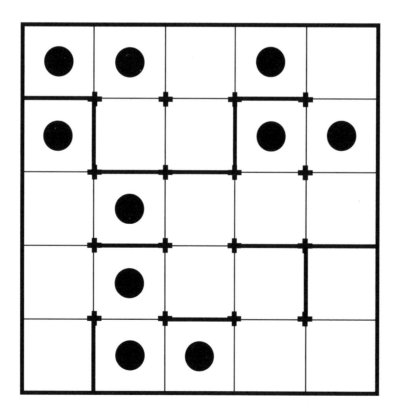

Shape Up

Every row and column in this grid originally contained one heart, one club, one diamond, one spade and two blank squares, although not necessarily in that order.

Every symbol with a black arrow refers to the first of the four symbols encountered when looking in the direction of the arrow. Every symbol with a white arrow refers to the second of the four symbols encountered in the direction of the arrow.

Can you complete the original grid?

Total Concentration

The blank squares below should be filled with whole numbers between 1 and 30 inclusive, any of which may occur more than once, or not at all.

The numbers in every horizontal row add up to the totals on the right, as do the two long diagonal lines; whilst those in every vertical column add up to the totals along the bottom.

							118
	28	5	2	15	18		107
6			27	24	11	19	117
16	21	23		1	30	12	106
25	30	6		4	14		117
	2		26	8	19	3	107
9		7	5			13	101
21		14	25	17		10	116
123	144	78	103	81	142	100	131

Logi-6

Every row and column of this grid should contain one each of the letters A, B, C, D, E, and F. Each of the six shapes (marked by thicker lines) should also contain one each of the letters A, B, C, D, E, and F.

Can you complete the grid?

				B	A
D				C	
F		E			

Hexagony

Can you place the hexagons into the grid, so that where any hexagon touches another along a straight line, the number in both triangles is the same? No rotation of any hexagon is allowed!

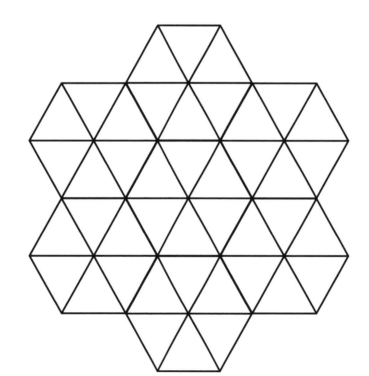

Ls in Place

Twelve L-shapes like the ones here need to be inserted in the grid and each L has one hole in it.

There are three pieces of each of the four kinds shown here and any piece may be turned or flipped over before being put in the grid. No pieces of the same kind touch, even at a corner.

The pieces fit together so well that you cannot see any spaces between them; only the holes show.

Can you tell where the Ls are?

Coin Collecting

In this puzzle, an amateur coin collector has been out with his metal detector, searching for booty. He didn't have time to dig up all the coins he found, so has made a grid map, showing their locations, in the hope that if he loses the map, at least no-one else will understand it…

Those squares containing numbers are empty, but where a number appears in a square, it indicates how many coins are located in the squares (up to a maximum of eight) surrounding the numbered one, touching it at any corner or side. There is only one coin in any individual square.

Place a circle into every square containing a coin.

1		3		3		3	3		
								3	1
	2	3			3				1
2				2		1			
2		1							1
	2		0						
	2		0			1	1		
		2			3		3		
2			3				4		1
		2			3			1	

129

Latin Square

The grid should be filled with numbers from 1 to 6, so that each number appears just once in every row and column.

The clues refer to the digit totals in the squares, eg A 1 2 3 = 6 means that the numbers in squares A1, A2 and A3 add up to 6.

	A	B	C	D	E	F
1						
2						
3						
4						
5						
6						

1 B C 2 = 5

2 A B C 3 = 13

3 E F 4 = 11

4 D E 5 = 5

5 B C D 6 = 11

6 A 4 5 = 9

7 B 4 5 = 4

8 C 4 5 = 6

9 D 1 2 = 11

10 E 2 3 = 10

11 F 5 6 = 7

Simple as A, B, C?

Each of the small squares in the grid below contains either A, B or C. Each row, column, and diagonal line of six squares has exactly two of each letter.

Can you tell the letter in each square?

	1	2	3	4	5	6
1						
2						
3						
4						
5						
6						

Across

1 The As are between the Bs

2 The Bs are further right than the As

3 The As are further right than the Bs

4 The As are further right than the Bs

5 The Cs are further right than the As

6 The Bs are next to each other

Down

1 No two letters the same are directly next to each other

3 The As are between the Cs

6 The As are lower than the Cs

Zigzag

The object of this puzzle is to trace a single path from the top left corner to the bottom right corner of the grid, moving through all of the cells in either a horizontal, vertical or diagonal direction.

Every cell must be entered once only and your path should take you through the numbers in the sequence 1-2-3-4-1-2-3-4, etc.

Can you find the way?

1	3	2	1	3	1	4	2
4	2	4	3	4	2	3	1
1	1	3	1	4	4	3	4
2	2	2	3	4	2	1	3
4	3	4	1	1	1	4	2
1	3	2	2	3	4	2	3
4	2	2	1	1	3	3	1
3	1	4	3	2	2	4	4

132

Battleships

Can you place the vessels into the diagram? Some parts of vessels or sea squares have already been filled in. A number to the right or below a row or column refers to the number of occupied squares in that row or column.

Any vessel may be positioned horizontally or vertically, but no part of a vessel touches part of any other vessel, either horizontally, vertically or diagonally.

Empty Area of Sea:

Aircraft Carrier:

Battleships:

Cruisers:

Submarines:

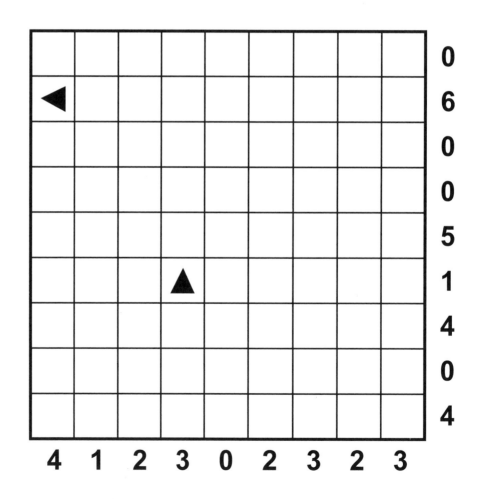

Slitherlink

Draw a single continuous loop, by connecting the dots.
No line may cross the path of another.

The figure inside each set of any four surrounding dots
indicates the total number of surrounding lines.

```
. . . . . . . . . .
  2 1 1 1 3 2 2
. . . . . . . . . .
        0           3
. . . . . . . . . .
      2 0   2 1 3
. . . . . . . . . .
 1 3   3   3     1
. . . . . . . . . .
   3           2
. . . . . . . . . .
 1 1       1       1
. . . . . . . . . .
 2       0   2   1 2
. . . . . . . . . .
 3     0 2     1 0
. . . . . . . . . .
        2 2     2 1
. . . . . . . . . .
 1   0     1
. . . . . . . . . .
 3           1 2 1
. . . . . . . . . .
   1   1   1 1
. . . . . . . . . .
```

Combiku

Each horizontal row and vertical column should contain different shapes and different numbers.

Every square will contain one number and one shape and no combination may be repeated anywhere else in the puzzle.

◇ ◯ ☆ ⬡ ▢
1   2   3   4   5

Mind Over Matter

Given that the letters are valued 1-26 according to their places in the alphabet, can you crack the mystery code to reveal the missing letter?

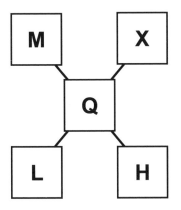

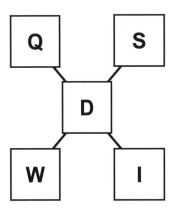

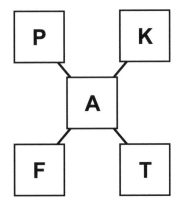

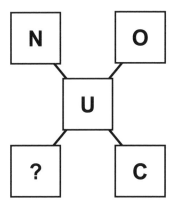

★★★

Tile Twister

Place the eight tiles into the puzzle grid so that all adjacent numbers on each tile match up. Tiles may be rotated through 360 degrees, but none may be flipped over.

1	2
4	3

2	1
3	3

4	4
1	1

1	4
1	2

1	3
2	2

		4	3		
		1	3		

2	4
3	3

2	3
1	1

1	2
4	2

It Doesn't Add Up

In the square below, change the positions of six numbers, one per horizontal row, vertical column and long diagonal line of six smaller squares, in such a way that the numbers in each row, column and long diagonal line total exactly 223.

Any number may appear more than once in a row, column or line.

38	8	33	31	68	48
47	37	35	30	38	42
43	56	37	40	27	27
37	58	38	41	33	41
5	43	53	37	30	25
23	24	33	51	52	29

Pyramid Plus

Every brick in this pyramid contains a number which is the sum of the two numbers below it, so that F=A+B, etc.

Just work out the missing numbers!

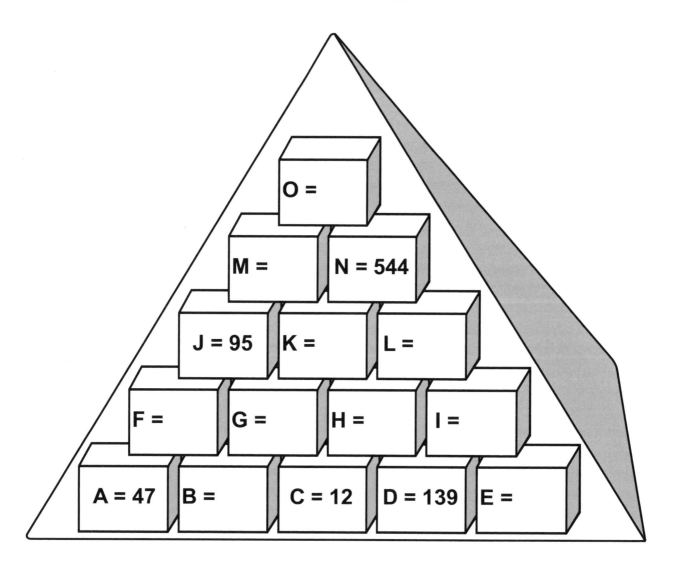

O =

M =   N = 544

J = 95   K =   L =

F =   G =   H =   I =

A = 47   B =   C = 12   D = 139   E =

Treasure Hunt

The chart gives directions to a hidden treasure behind the black square in the grid. Move the indicated number of spaces north, south, east and west (eg 4N means move four squares north) stopping at every square once only to arrive there. At which square should you start?

N

⇧

2E	1W	2E	3S	1S
3S	1W	2S	1N	1W
1E	2E	■	1W	2S
1E	3N	2W	1S	1N
2N	3N	3N	2W	2W

W ⇦   ⇨ E

⇩

S

Symbol Sums

Each symbol stands for a different number. In order to reach the correct total at the end of each row and column, what is the value of the circle, cross, pentagon, square and star?

■	✚	✚	★	★	= 35
✚	■	●	✚	✚	= 40
★	★	■	✚	⬠	= 30
★	✚	■	■	⬠	= 32
⬠	■	✚	⬠	■	= 31
=	=	=	=	=	
30	37	38	34	29	

Missing Number

In the grid below, what number should replace the question mark?

3	4	6	18	8	1	2
9	7	5	2	3	4	14
1	3	5	7	22	3	5
19	16	1	2	1	4	5
8	6	13	4	5	11	3
2	4	16	6	9	5	10
6	17	12	3	8	4	?

Hidato

Starting at 1 and finishing at 49, track your way from one square to another, either horizontally, vertically, or diagonally, placing consecutive numbers into the empty squares as you go.

43	44	49	46	47	17	
		45				
	40	41	19	14	8	
		31				
	30	28	32			12
35		33				
1	34		4		25	23

Sum Total

Fill each empty square so that every row contains ten different numbers from 0 to 9. In columns the numbers may be repeated, but wherever one square touches another, whether horizontally, vertically, or diagonally, the numbers must be different. Some are already in place.

The black squares show the sum total of the numbers in each column.

	6		8			0		1	7
		2		3	7		5		4
4		5	9	6				8	
3	9	2	1				5		
			7		4	0			2
8		4	1	5				7	
31	**23**	**23**	**27**	**34**	**32**	**14**	**27**	**34**	**25**

Number Link

Working from one square to another, horizontally or vertically (never diagonally), draw single continuous paths to pair up each set of two matching numbers.

No line may cross another, none may travel through any square containing a number, and every square must be visited just once.

	16	14							5
	2		6	12		7	6		11
				14			5		
			3	12				17	
	10			15			7		11
16		2	3		1		4		8
18		1			9			17	
			10	19		15		4	
			18		9	8			
19					13				13

Domino Placement

A standard set of 28 dominoes has been laid out as shown. Can you draw in the edges of them all?

The check-box is provided as an aid, and the domino already placed will help.

6	1	6	6	1	3	4
3	5	3	5	5	2	4
4	5	1	2	0	3	2
1	0	2	5	6	0	1
1	0	3	2	2	3	5
6	5	3	1	0	2	4
3	1	4	5	6	6	0
4	6	4	0	2	4	0

0-0	0-1	0-2	0-3	0-4	0-5	0-6	1-1	1-2	1-3	1-4	1-5	1-6	2-2

2-3	2-4	2-5	2-6	3-3	3-4	3-5	3-6	4-4	4-5	4-6	5-5	5-6	6-6
		✔											

Light Up

Place circles (representing light bulbs) in some of the empty squares, in such a way that no two bulbs shine on each other, until every square of the grid is lit up. A bulb sends rays of light horizontally and vertically, illuminating its entire row and column unless its light is blocked by a black cell.

Some black cells contain numbers, indicating how many light bulbs are in adjacent squares either immediately above, below, to the right, or to the left. Bulbs placed diagonally adjacent to a numbered cell do not contribute to the bulb count. An unnumbered black cell may have any number of light bulbs adjacent to it, or none at all, and not all light bulbs are necessarily clued via black squares.

Skyscrapers

Place the numbers 1 to 6 into each row and column, one number per square. Each number represents a skyscraper of that many floors.

Arrange the skyscrapers in such a way that the given number outside the grid represents the number of buildings which can be seen from that point, looking only at that number's row or column.

A skyscraper with a lower number of floors cannot hide a higher building, but one with a higher number of floors always hides any building behind it.

	3	2		2	4	2	
2							3
2							3
5				3			
			2				3
							2
3							2
	3	4	2	2			

Brickwork

Every square should be filled with a number from 1 to 8.
No number may appear twice in any row or column.

Every brick that consists of two squares contains both
an odd number and an even number.

6			8			2	
	7		4				
8				2			6
4	2		3				5
5	6					1	
				3			
	4			7		8	
7		8	5			6	2

No Three in Line

Place either O or X into each empty square, so that no three consecutive squares in either a horizontal row or vertical column contain more than two of the same symbol.

There needs to be as many Os as Xs in every row and column.

		O		X		X	X
	O			O		X	
X							X
	O		O		X	O	
X					X	X	
			O				X
X			X	O			O
X	X				X		

Calcudoku

Each row and column should contain six different numbers from 1 to 6.

The numbers placed in a heavily outlined set of squares may be repeated, but must produce the calculation in the top left corner, using the mathematical symbol provided: multiply (x), divide (/), add (+), and subtract (−).

For example, when multiplied, the numbers 4 and 3 total 12:

12x	
4	**3**

5/		10+		3−	2/
4+		40x	6x		
9+				6/	
	7+		6/		40x
3/	18x	30x			
			4/		

Shape Sorter

The grid below is divided into regions of three squares.
Some need to contain three different shapes: a circle, a square,
and a triangle; others need to contain three identical shapes.

When two squares share a side across a region
boundary, the shapes must be different.

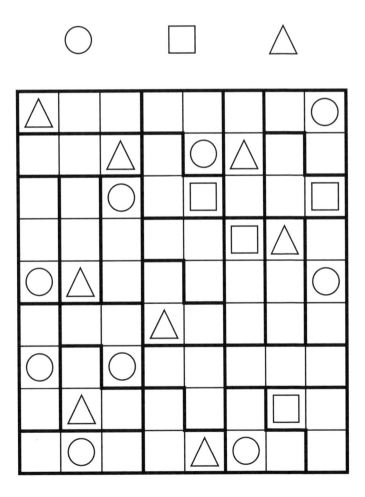

Logi-6

Every row and column of this grid should contain one each of the letters A, B, C, D, E, and F.

In addition, each of the six shapes (marked by thicker lines) should also contain one each of the letters A, B, C, D, E, and F.

Can you complete the grid?

	B			C	
		D	E		
B			C		
					B
	A			D	C
		F		E	

Chains

Fill each empty circle with one of the numbers 1-7.

Every horizontal row, vertical column, set of seven linked circles, and diagonal line of seven circles should contain seven different numbers.

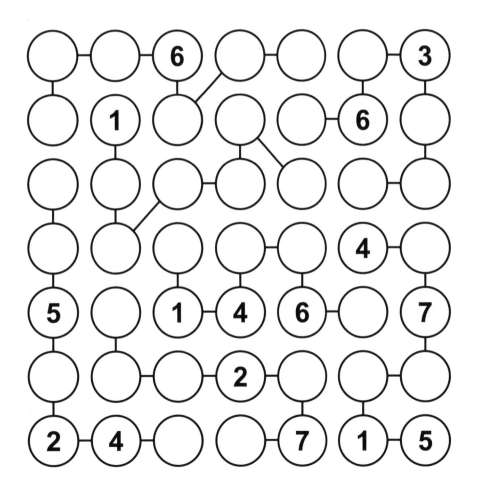

Coin Collecting

In this puzzle, an amateur coin collector has been out with his metal detector, searching for booty. He didn't have time to dig up all the coins he found, so has made a grid map, showing their locations, in the hope that if he loses the map, at least no-one else will understand it…

Those squares containing numbers are empty, but where a number appears in a square, it indicates how many coins are located in the squares (up to a maximum of eight) surrounding the numbered one, touching it at any corner or side. There is only one coin in any individual square.

Place a circle into every square containing a coin.

	3				4		
		5	4			4	
	5				4		2
		3					1
	4		5		5		
		2	4			3	2
2			3				
	3	2			3	2	3
1				2		2	

Patchwork

Every square should be filled with a letter from A to E, and each heavily outlined set of five squares should contain five different letters. Every row and column must contain two of each letter.

Squares that share a common border may not contain the same letter.

	D				C	D	B		
			C	D		B			
B		E		B		E	C		
		B	D				D		
			C	D	E			E	
D				E	B	A			B
		C			D		A		E
	E					C			D
D		C							
A					D				E

Battleships

★★★★

Can you place the vessels into the diagram? Some parts of vessels or sea squares have already been filled in. A number to the right or below a row or column refers to the number of occupied squares in that row or column.

Any vessel may be positioned horizontally or vertically, but no part of a vessel touches part of any other vessel, either horizontally, vertically or diagonally.

Empty Area of Sea:

Aircraft Carrier:

Battleships:

Cruisers:

Submarines:

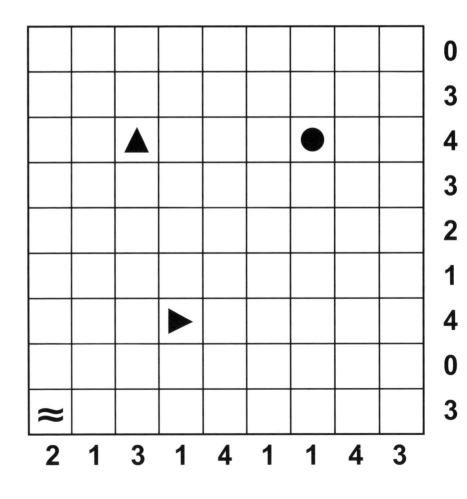

Slitherlink

Draw a single continuous loop, by connecting the dots.
No line may cross the path of another.

The figure inside each set of any four surrounding dots
indicates the total number of surrounding lines.

```
·   ·   ·   ·   ·   ·   ·   ·   ·   ·
  3   2       2               3
·   ·   ·   ·   ·   ·   ·   ·   ·   ·
  2       3               2   1   2
·   ·   ·   ·   ·   ·   ·   ·   ·   ·
  2                       0       2
·   ·   ·   ·   ·   ·   ·   ·   ·   ·
  3   2   1   3       2   2
·   ·   ·   ·   ·   ·   ·   ·   ·   ·
  2               1   1   3       3
·   ·   ·   ·   ·   ·   ·   ·   ·   ·
  3               3           1
·   ·   ·   ·   ·   ·   ·   ·   ·   ·
  2       1   2   2   1
·   ·   ·   ·   ·   ·   ·   ·   ·   ·
  3           3       2           2
·   ·   ·   ·   ·   ·   ·   ·   ·   ·
  1   2           2       2       2
·   ·   ·   ·   ·   ·   ·   ·   ·   ·
```

Combiku

Each horizontal row and vertical column should contain different shapes and different numbers.

Every square will contain one number and one shape and no combination may be repeated anywhere else in the puzzle.

◇ 1   ○ 2   ☆ 3   ⬡ 4   □ 5

Bridges

Join the circular islands by drawing horizontal or vertical lines to represent bridges, in such a way that the number of bridges connected to each island must match the number on that island. No bridge may cross another, and no more than two bridges can join any pair of islands.

The finished design will allow you to travel from one island to any other island on the map.

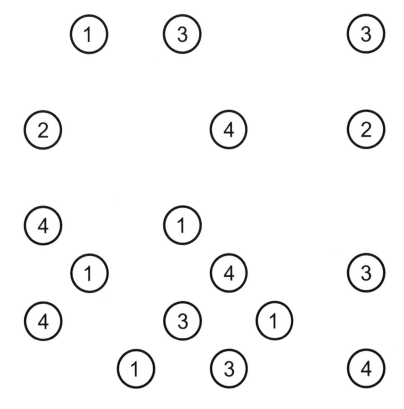

No Four in Line

Place either O or X into each empty square, so that no four consecutive squares in a straight line in any direction (horizontally, vertically, or diagonally) contain more than three of the same symbol.

O	X		O				X	X	
O	X				O				O
X			O		X	X	X		X
	X		O		X		X	X	X
	X								
					O		X		X
	X			O	X				O
	X	X					X		
X			O		X		X		O
	X			X	X		X	X	O
X	X		O		O			O	X

Futoshiki

Fill the grid so that every horizontal row and vertical
column contains all the numbers 1 to 7.

Any arrows in the grid always point toward a square that contains a lower number.

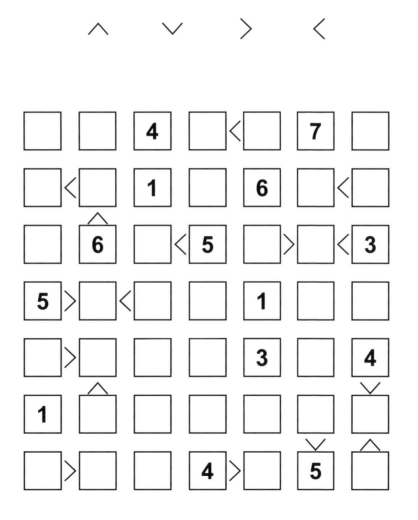

Hidato

Starting at 1 and finishing at 49, track your way from one square to another, either horizontally, vertically, or diagonally, placing consecutive numbers into the empty squares as you go.

		20		17	14	
	49					
				22	12	
37		31			10	
	36			25	7	9
	42	29		1	4	
40		27		3		

Sum Total

Fill each empty square so that every row contains ten different numbers from 0 to 9. In columns the numbers may be repeated, but wherever one square touches another, whether horizontally, vertically, or diagonally, the numbers must be different. Some are already in place.

The black squares show the sum total of the numbers in each column.

5			3		4		6		
4	7	5		0	8	3			
9	8			6					2
4	6		0	9	2			5	
	5	9	1	7			4		
		6			9			7	1
27	**39**	**26**	**22**	**25**	**38**	**12**	**27**	**29**	**25**

Number Link

Working from one square to another, horizontally or vertically (never diagonally), draw single continuous paths to pair up each set of two matching numbers.

No line may cross another, none may travel through any square containing a number, and every square must be visited just once.

7								7	3	4
5								3		
8		6	1		11					
			5		2			11		
	14		14			10			6	
		8								
9						13				10
		13			1					
							15		4	
9					12					
12		2								15

Domino Placement

A standard set of 28 dominoes has been laid out as shown. Can you draw in the edges of them all?

The check-box is provided as an aid, so that you can see which dominoes have been located.

2	3	1	4	2	2	2
6	3	5	4	2	6	5
1	0	3	1	6	0	0
5	5	6	6	2	0	3
4	6	0	2	5	4	4
6	5	1	5	5	3	4
3	0	0	4	3	3	6
1	2	1	1	1	0	4

0-0	0-1	0-2	0-3	0-4	0-5	0-6	1-1	1-2	1-3	1-4	1-5	1-6	2-2

2-3	2-4	2-5	2-6	3-3	3-4	3-5	3-6	4-4	4-5	4-6	5-5	5-6	6-6

Light Up

Place circles (representing light bulbs) in some of the empty squares, in such a way that no two bulbs shine on each other, until every square of the grid is lit up. A bulb sends rays of light horizontally and vertically, illuminating its entire row and column unless its light is blocked by a black cell.

Some black cells contain numbers, indicating how many light bulbs are in adjacent squares either immediately above, below, to the right, or to the left. Bulbs placed diagonally adjacent to a numbered cell do not contribute to the bulb count. An unnumbered black cell may have any number of light bulbs adjacent to it, or none at all, and not all light bulbs are necessarily clued via black squares.

Skyscrapers

Place the numbers 1 to 6 into each row and column, one number per square. Each number represents a skyscraper of that many floors.

Arrange the skyscrapers in such a way that the given number outside the grid represents the number of buildings which can be seen from that point, looking only at that number's row or column.

A skyscraper with a lower number of floors cannot hide a higher building, but one with a higher number of floors always hides any building behind it.

	2	5		3	1	
2						
			3			
2						
4						3
2						4
1						
		2				

Brickwork

Every square should be filled with a number from 1 to 8.
No number may appear twice in any row or column.

Every brick that consists of two squares contains both
an odd number and an even number.

					8		3
1		5					
					3	1	8
		8		4			
			6	5			1
	3					7	
		4		2	7		
		7	8			2	

No Three in Line

Place either O or X into each empty square, so that no three consecutive squares in either a horizontal row or vertical column contain more than two of the same symbol.

There needs to be as many Os as Xs in every row and column.

X							
X	O					X	X
			O		O		
	X					O	
			O			O	
				O	X		
		O				O	O

Calcudoku

Each row and column should contain seven different numbers from 1 to 7.

The numbers placed in a heavily outlined set of squares may be repeated, but must produce the calculation in the top left corner, using the mathematical symbol provided: multiply (x), divide (/), add (+), and subtract (−).

For example, when multiplied, the numbers 4 and 3 total 12:

12x	
4	**3**

2/	1−	10+	140x		7+	
				12x		11+
2/	70x		2/		13+	
	10+		42x			168x
		4/		15x		
30x				4−		
1−		9+		2x		

Shape Sorter

The grid below is divided into regions of three squares.
Some need to contain three different shapes: a circle, a square,
and a triangle; others need to contain three identical shapes.

When two squares share a side across a region
boundary, the shapes must be different.

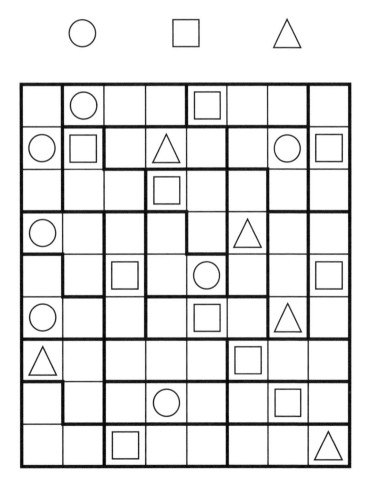

Logi-6

Every row and column of this grid should contain one
each of the letters A, B, C, D, E, and F.

In addition, each of the six shapes (marked by thicker lines) should
also contain one each of the letters A, B, C, D, E, and F.

Can you complete the grid?

	C	B		F	
	A				
E					D
		A			
			B		

Chains

Fill each empty circle with one of the numbers 1-7.

Every horizontal row, vertical column, set of seven linked circles, and diagonal line of seven circles should contain seven different numbers.

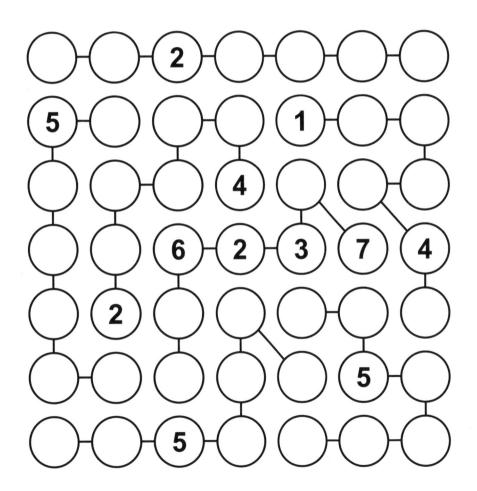

Coin Collecting

In this puzzle, an amateur coin collector has been out with his metal detector, searching for booty. He didn't have time to dig up all the coins he found, so has made a grid map, showing their locations, in the hope that if he loses the map, at least no-one else will understand it…

Those squares containing numbers are empty, but where a number appears in a square, it indicates how many coins are located in the squares (up to a maximum of eight) surrounding the numbered one, touching it at any corner or side. There is only one coin in any individual square.

Place a circle into every square containing a coin.

1	2			1		1	
1			3		2		2
		4		3		3	
2		3		4			
	4		4			3		3
3		3				3		3
2			2		4		3	
2		2			2			2
			2			1		

Patchwork

Every square should be filled with a letter from A to E, and each heavily outlined set of five squares should contain five different letters. Every row and column must contain two of each letter.

Squares that share a common border may not contain the same letter.

		D			E				B
		A					D		
	A								
				B			B		E
D				D		A			
B	C			B					A
		E						B	
C	D		B					A	
		E			D				
				E			A		D

Battleships

Can you place the vessels into the diagram? Some parts of vessels or sea squares have already been filled in. A number to the right or below a row or column refers to the number of occupied squares in that row or column.

Any vessel may be positioned horizontally or vertically, but no part of a vessel touches part of any other vessel, either horizontally, vertically or diagonally.

Empty Area of Sea:

Aircraft Carrier:

Battleships:

Cruisers:

Submarines:

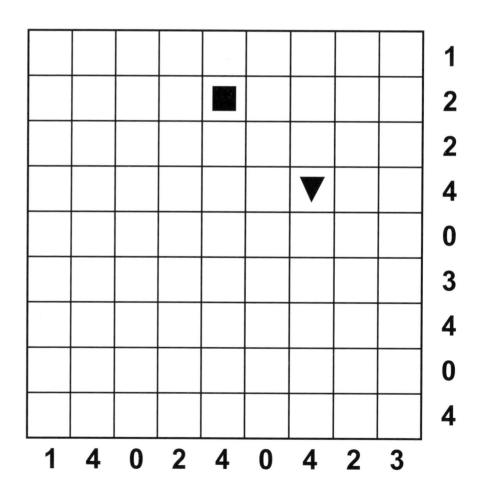

Slitherlink

Draw a single continuous loop, by connecting the dots.
No line may cross the path of another.

The figure inside each set of any four surrounding dots
indicates the total number of surrounding lines.

```
3         1         3   3
2   1     1                 3
3   3     2     2     3
    2     3   1             3
        2   2     1   2   1     1
3       3     3   1         1   2
            1     1         3
3   2   2                     3
1       0     3     3     2
2           2   1   0   1     1   3
            1   1         1   2
```

Combiku

Each horizontal row and vertical column should contain different shapes and different numbers.

Every square will contain one number and one shape and no combination may be repeated anywhere else in the puzzle.

◇ 1   ○ 2   ☆ 3   ⬡ 4   ☐ 5

⬡	2			◇
3		4		
4			5	☐
2		☆		⬡ 5
	○	☐		

Bridges

Join the circular islands by drawing horizontal or vertical lines to represent bridges, in such a way that the number of bridges connected to each island must match the number on that island. No bridge may cross another, and no more than two bridges can join any pair of islands.

The finished design will allow you to travel from one island to any other island on the map.

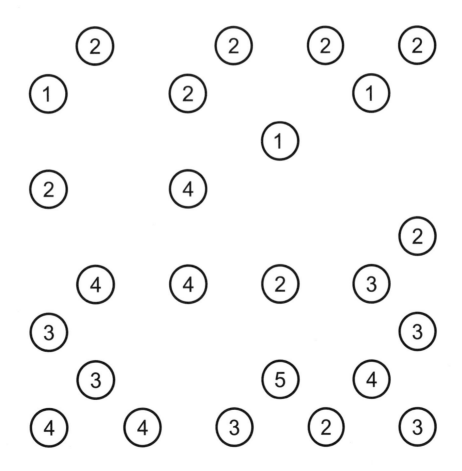

No Four in Line

Place either O or X into each empty square, so that no four consecutive squares in a straight line in any direction (horizontally, vertically, or diagonally) contain more than three of the same symbol.

	X		O		O					
	X	X			X		X	O	X	
	X		X					O	O	
O					X		X			
	X				X		O			
	X	X			X		X		X	
								X	X	
O	X				O	O				
O							O			
							O		O	
O		O	O				X			

Futoshiki

Fill the grid so that every horizontal row and vertical
column contains all the numbers 1 to 7.

Any arrows in the grid always point toward a square that contains a lower number.

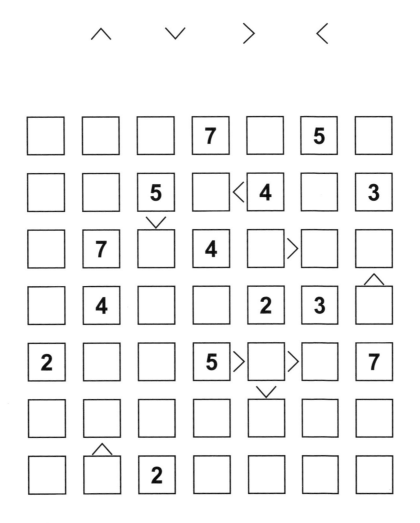

Hidato

Starting at 1 and finishing at 64, track your way from one square to another, either horizontally, vertically, or diagonally, placing consecutive numbers into the empty squares as you go.

	5	3	2		23	19	
			1			20	
64	8	62		27			
60			11				
59		10		29			32
	57	56	54		39		
	50	51	52			40	34
				42	41	36	

Sum Total

Fill each empty square so that every row contains ten different numbers from 0 to 9. In columns the numbers may be repeated, but wherever one square touches another, whether horizontally, vertically, or diagonally, the numbers must be different. Some are already in place.

The black squares show the sum total of the numbers in each column.

	9	0		4			3		
4		5			0			2	8
9	1	3			8			6	5
		8	6		3				4
	7					2	1		
8				2					
25	**25**	**30**	**33**	**23**	**32**	**29**	**20**	**30**	**23**

Number Link

Working from one square to another, horizontally or vertically (never diagonally), draw single continuous paths to pair up each set of two matching numbers.

No line may cross another, none may travel through any square containing a number, and every square must be visited just once.

	4									10
	10		2							2
				5						5
		6				7				11
4							1		8	
		6			9					
						3			
			9			1			
7	11								8	3

Domino Placement

A set of 36 dominoes has been laid out as shown. Can you draw in the edges of them all?

The check-box is provided as an aid, so that you can see which dominoes have been located.

2	5	2	7	0	1	1	2
4	3	0	4	5	3	4	2
1	6	7	6	0	1	0	2
7	6	5	4	3	7	5	7
7	6	1	0	2	6	1	4
6	7	6	5	6	5	1	7
3	3	1	3	4	0	2	0
2	6	5	5	0	2	5	7
3	3	3	1	0	4	4	4

0-0	0-1	0-2	0-3	0-4	0-5	0-6	0-7	1-1	1-2	1-3	1-4	1-5	1-6	1-7	2-2	2-3	2-4

2-5	2-6	2-7	3-3	3-4	3-5	3-6	3-7	4-4	4-5	4-6	4-7	5-5	5-6	5-7	6-6	6-7	7-7

Light Up

Place circles (representing light bulbs) in some of the empty squares, in such a way that no two bulbs shine on each other, until every square of the grid is lit up. A bulb sends rays of light horizontally and vertically, illuminating its entire row and column unless its light is blocked by a black cell.

Some black cells contain numbers, indicating how many light bulbs are in adjacent squares either immediately above, below, to the right, or to the left. Bulbs placed diagonally adjacent to a numbered cell do not contribute to the bulb count. An unnumbered black cell may have any number of light bulbs adjacent to it, or none at all, and not all light bulbs are necessarily clued via black squares.

Skyscrapers

Place the numbers 1 to 7 into each row and column, one number per square. Each number represents a skyscraper of that many floors.

Arrange the skyscrapers in such a way that the given number outside the grid represents the number of buildings which can be seen from that point, looking only at that number's row or column.

A skyscraper with a lower number of floors cannot hide a higher building, but one with a higher number of floors always hides any building behind it.

	1	4	3	3			
		3					2
5	3				1		1
1					2		4
3				7			2
	6			5	3		4
2		4		3			
	3	4	3	1		4	

Brickwork

Every square should be filled with a number from 1 to 9.
No number may appear twice in any row or column.

Every brick that consists of two squares contains both
an odd number and an even number.

2	7				4			
			2		8		9	
		1		3				
			6					
4		9					5	
1							3	2
				6	9			3
7		4				6		
9						3		7

No Three in Line

Place either O or X into each empty square, so that no three consecutive squares in either a horizontal row or vertical column contain more than two of the same symbol.

There needs to be as many Os as Xs in every row and column.

O									
		O		X			O		
			O		O		O	O	
	X			X					
	O								
X									X
							X		
		O	O					O	
X	X		X	X					

Calcudoku

Each row and column should contain seven different numbers from 1 to 8.

The numbers placed in a heavily outlined set of squares may be repeated, but must produce the calculation in the top left corner, using the mathematical symbol provided: multiply (x), divide (/), add (+), and subtract (−).

For example, when multiplied, the numbers 4 and 3 total 12:

12x	
4	**3**

5/		24x	10+		8x	42x	
21x			10+			5/	
	60x			1−		12x	
112x		13+			19+	10+	
	32x		10+	6/		1−	
10+		7/					48x
2−			2/	8+		48x	
	1−			7/			

Shape Sorter

The grid below is divided into regions of three squares.
Some need to contain three different shapes: a circle, a square,
and a triangle; others need to contain three identical shapes.

When two squares share a side across a region
boundary, the shapes must be different.

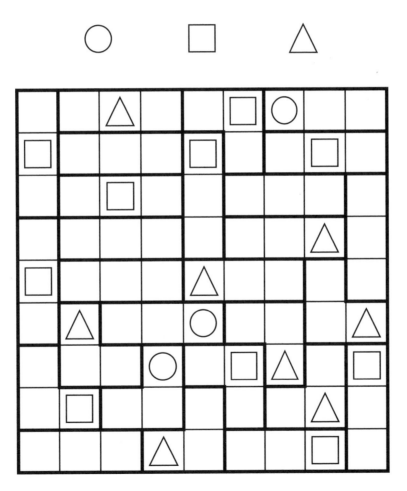

Logi-7

Every row and column of this grid should contain one
each of the letters A, B, C, D, E, F, and G.

In addition, each of the seven shapes (marked by thicker lines) should
also contain one each of the letters A, B, C, D, E, F, and G.

Can you complete the grid?

C						
A					B	F
		E			D	
				B		A
	C		A			
	D		G		A	

Chains

Fill each empty circle with one of the numbers 1-8.

Every horizontal row, vertical column, set of eight linked circles, and diagonal line of eight circles should contain eight different numbers.

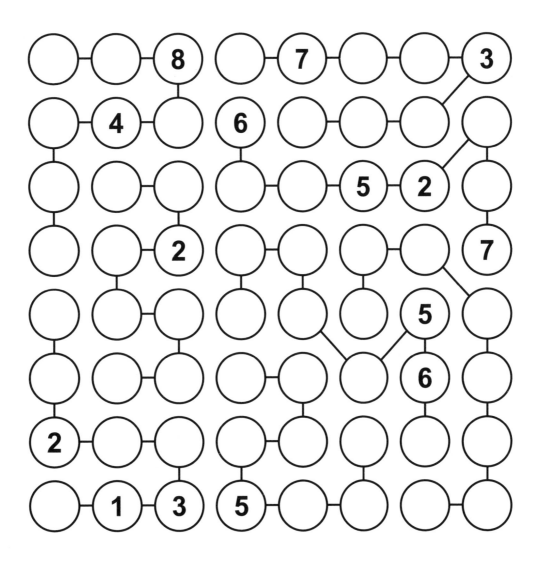

Coin Collecting

In this puzzle, an amateur coin collector has been out with his metal detector, searching for booty. He didn't have time to dig up all the coins he found, so has made a grid map, showing their locations, in the hope that if he loses the map, at least no-one else will understand it…

Those squares containing numbers are empty, but where a number appears in a square, it indicates how many coins are located in the squares (up to a maximum of eight) surrounding the numbered one, touching it at any corner or side. There is only one coin in any individual square.

Place a circle into every square containing a coin.

		3		2		3			1	
4		5	2			3				2
2		3		3					6	
			3		2		5			
2			3			3				
	4						3		3	
3				3	2	2				4
						2		4		
		6			4			3		
4			4			2				1
2		2							3	

Patchwork

Every square should be filled with a letter from A to F, and each heavily outlined set of six squares should contain six different letters. Every row and column must contain two of each letter.

Squares that share a common border may not contain the same letter.

				C				C	A		
F				E		C		D			B
		C				B		F	A	E	
	D		F				C		F		
					F				B	D	A
		A			A		B				
		A				A					B
D	A					E	C	F		F	
			E		D	A			C	E	
	C		A					A		D	
		F			B						
		D	B	C	A		B		E		D

Battleships

Can you place the vessels into the diagram? Some parts of vessels or sea squares have already been filled in. A number to the right or below a row or column refers to the number of occupied squares in that row or column.

Any vessel may be positioned horizontally or vertically, but no part of a vessel touches part of any other vessel, either horizontally, vertically or diagonally.

Empty Area of Sea:

Aircraft Carrier:

Battleships:

Cruisers:

Submarines:

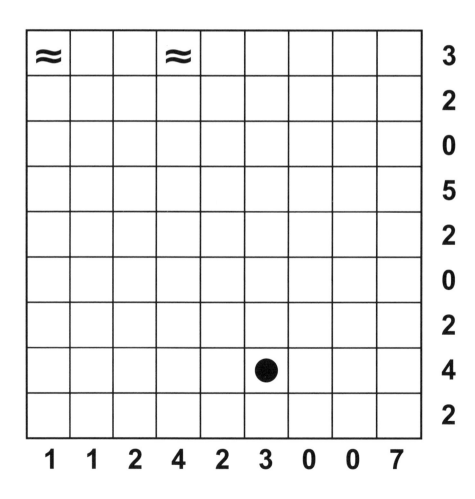

Slitherlink

Draw a single continuous loop, by connecting the dots.
No line may cross the path of another.

The figure inside each set of any four surrounding dots
indicates the total number of surrounding lines.

Combiku

Each horizontal row and vertical column should contain different shapes and different numbers.

Every square will contain one number and one shape and no combination may be repeated anywhere else in the puzzle.

◇ 1   ○ 2   ☆ 3   ⬡ 4   ☐ 5

Bridges

Join the circular islands by drawing horizontal or vertical lines to represent bridges, in such a way that the number of bridges connected to each island must match the number on that island. No bridge may cross another, and no more than two bridges can join any pair of islands.

The finished design will allow you to travel from one island to any other island on the map.

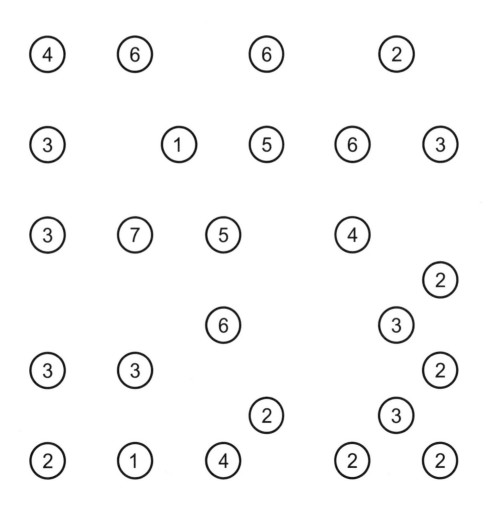

No Four in Line

Place either O or X into each empty square, so that no four consecutive squares in a straight line in any direction (horizontally, vertically, or diagonally) contain more than three of the same symbol.

X		X		O	X		O	
	O			X				
X	O		X		O	O		
	O				O			O
X						O		O
X		X						
	O							O
			X		X	O		X
				X	O			O
X	O						X	
X	O					X		
O	O		O		X		X	O
O		X		X		O		

Futoshiki

Fill the grid so that every horizontal row and vertical
column contains all the numbers 1 to 8.

Any arrows in the grid always point toward a square that contains a lower number.

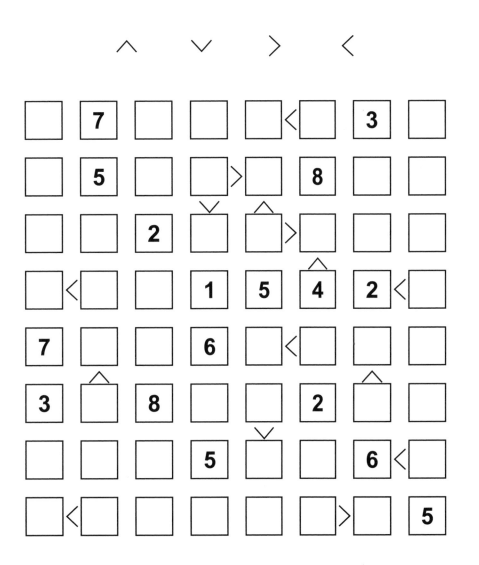

1

		4	5						
	1	2	6	6					
	0	3	0	1					
1	6	0	5	4	6	3	2		
1	4	2	2	3	6	5	2	6	0
0	4	1	5	2	6	1	3	4	4
2	4	0	2	3	5	3	3		
	3	4	0	1					
	5	6	0	1					
		5	5						

2

3

4

14	25	11	9	37	32	34	2
10	11	13	5	34	25	2	26
35	26	39	6	5	1	22	25
1	18	21	34	40	7	27	15
26	21	23	27	19	34	19	11
37	16	30	34	11	34	2	24
15	1	37	38	30	20	6	4
6	12	8	33	22	21	10	4

5 The minute hand moves forward by 11 minutes and the hour hand moves back by 3 hours each time.

6

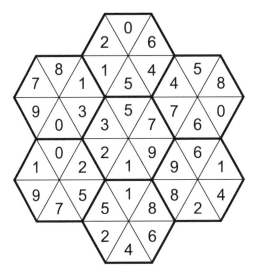

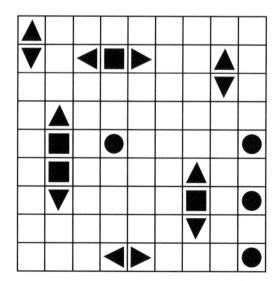

9

6	3	1	2	5	4
1	6	2	4	3	5
3	1	5	6	4	2
5	4	3	1	2	6
2	5	4	3	6	1
4	2	6	5	1	3

10

A	A	C	B	B	C
C	B	A	C	B	A
B	B	C	C	A	A
B	C	B	A	A	C
C	A	B	A	C	B
A	C	A	B	C	B

11

1	2	5	6	2	3
3	4	4	2	2	4
1	5	3	1	5	1
2	6	6	4	6	2
3	4	5	3	4	3
5	6	1	2	5	6

12

13

```
        3 1   1 2
      1 1       0 2
  2       1       1     2
  2 1 0         3 1
  2     1 1   3 1     1
      1 2             1
        1 3 1 2     1
        2 2
  3 3 2     1     1   1 2
        1             1 1
  3     3 1     1 0     2
        1     3 3
```

14

3 (hexagon)	4 (diamond)	5 (circle)	1 (square)	2 (star)
1 (diamond)	3 (star)	2 (square)	5 (hexagon)	4 (circle)
5 (star)	1 (circle)	4 (hexagon)	2 (diamond)	3 (square)
4 (square)	2 (hexagon)	1 (star)	3 (circle)	5 (diamond)
2 (circle)	5 (square)	3 (diamond)	4 (star)	1 (hexagon)

15 The value of the central letter is the total of the other four letters. Thus the missing value is 4, so the missing letter is D.

16

1	2	2	2	2	3
1	4	4	2	2	3
1	4	4	2	2	3
3	3	3	2	2	1
3	3	3	2	2	1
1	4	4	4	4	3

17

14	**21**	10	23	14	14
25	26	18	21	**2**	4
22	9	**6**	28	21	10
12	9	30	4	17	24
9	8	6	11	32	**30**
14	23	26	**9**	10	14

18 A=143, B=54, C=63, D=73, E=106, F=197, G=117, H=136, I=179, J=314, K=253, L=315, M=567, N=568, O=1135

19

1S	1E	2W	2W	1W
1E	1E	1E	1S	**1N**
2E	1S	■	1E	1S
1S	2E	2W	1W	1S
2N	2N	1E	2W	2W

20

4	1	**3**	2	5
1	**3**	5	4	**2**
3	**2**	4	5	1
5	4	2	1	3
2	5	1	3	4

21

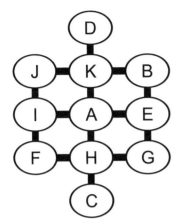

22

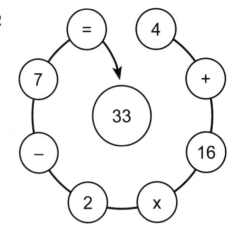

23

6						6
			7			
	5				1	
7			7		4	
6		9		5		1

24

8	+	5	x	9	=	117
−		−		x		
1	x	2	+	3	=	5
+		x		+		
6	+	4	−	7	=	3
=		=		=		
13		12		34		

25

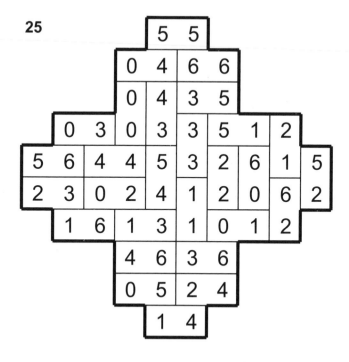

```
            5 5
          0 4 6 6
          0 4 3 5
    0 3   0 3 3 5 1   2
  5 6 4 4 5 3 2 6 1 5
  2 3 0 2 4 1 2 0 6 2
    1 6 1 3 1 0 1 2
          4 6 3 6
          0 5 2 4
            1 4
```

26

27

28

33	11	37	15	23	21	22	2
21	18	9	31	23	13	13	39
32	35	25	36	24	11	21	19
6	33	29	31	27	16	26	18
38	24	39	32	18	22	17	23
23	3	8	15	33	11	10	28
22	9	20	29	22	19	12	28
13	12	35	24	38	39	29	31

29

D	B	F	C	A	E
C	E	B	A	D	F
F	D	C	B	E	A
E	A	D	F	B	C
A	C	E	D	F	B
B	F	A	E	C	D

30

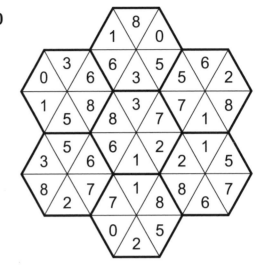

31

32

33

6	5	3	1	4	2
3	2	1	5	6	4
2	1	4	6	5	3
4	6	5	2	3	1
1	3	6	4	2	5
5	4	2	3	1	6

34

A	C	B	A	C	B
A	C	B	C	B	A
B	A	C	C	A	B
C	B	A	B	A	C
B	A	C	A	B	C
C	B	A	B	C	A

35

1	2	4	5	6	1
1	6	3	6	5	2
2	5	2	1	4	3
3	4	1	3	5	4
4	2	3	6	4	5
5	6	1	2	3	6

36

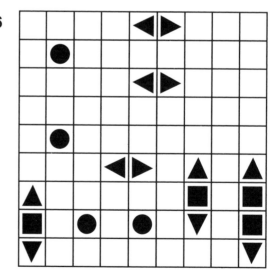

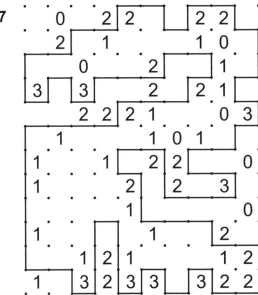

37

38

☆ 2	◯ 4	⬡ 5	◇ 3	▢ 1
◯ 3	⬡ 1	◇ 2	▢ 4	☆ 5
◇ 1	▢ 2	☆ 4	◯ 5	⬡ 3
▢ 5	☆ 3	◯ 1	⬡ 2	◇ 4
⬡ 4	◇ 5	▢ 3	☆ 1	◯ 2

39 The value of the central letter is the total value of the two letters in the highest boxes, minus the total value of the two letters in the lowest boxes. Thus the missing value is 2, so the missing letter is B.

40

4	1	1	3	3	1
2	4	4	4	4	2
2	4	4	4	4	2
3	1	1	2	2	3
3	1	1	2	2	3
1	2	2	2	2	4

41

53	**11**	14	36	42	21
14	31	34	50	**32**	16
34	36	**29**	29	27	22
33	47	58	3	9	27
33	27	2	33	26	**56**
10	25	40	**26**	41	35

42 A=86, B=67, C=75, D=121, E=68,
F=153, G=142, H=196, I=189, J=295,
K=338, L=385, M=633, N=723, O=1356.

43

1E	2S	2W	1W	1W
1S	1E	1W	1W	1S
1S	1E	■	1S	2N
2E	**1S**	2E	2N	2N
2E	1W	2E	2N	1W

44

5	4	1 < 2	3
1	**3** > 2	5 > 4
4	2	5	3 > 1
3	5	4	1	2
2 > 1	3	4	5

45

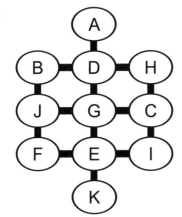

46

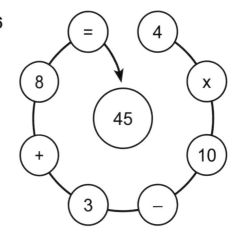

47

			8		2	
	3					
				9		6
9		2				
				5		1
2		8			5	

48

5	+	7	−	8	=	4
−	■	+	■	+		
1	x	9	+	2	=	11
x	■	−	■	−		
4	x	6	−	3	=	21
=		=		=		
16		10		7		

49

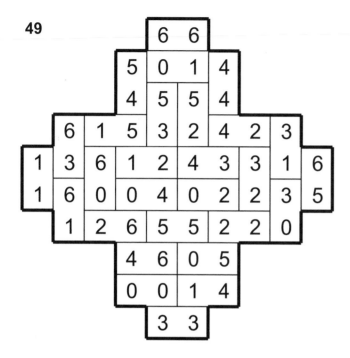

50

51

52

5	32	26	36	9	6	24	14
13	30	25	31	29	17	24	13
7	9	31	2	31	31	11	25
29	9	16	2	17	28	22	22
24	23	2	9	33	30	24	2
11	19	15	1	25	39	35	30
21	3	33	38	17	16	37	8
14	25	29	22	32	13	27	26

53 The hour hand alternately gains 3 and 7 hours and the minute hand alternately loses 7 and 3 minutes each time.

54

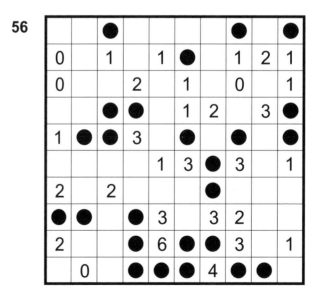

55

56

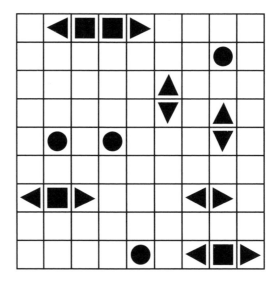

57

4	5	3	6	2	1
1	6	5	2	3	4
3	4	2	1	5	6
5	3	1	4	6	2
2	1	6	3	4	5
6	2	4	5	1	3

58

C	B	B	A	A	C
B	A	C	C	B	A
A	C	B	B	A	C
B	A	A	C	C	B
C	C	A	A	B	B
A	B	C	B	C	A

59

1	6	5	6	2	3
2	4	1	1	5	4
3	2	1	6	5	4
1	3	4	2	3	3
2	6	5	4	5	2
3	4	5	6	1	6

60

61

```
    0       3    1
  1     1 1 0        0 2
              0        0 2
  1                    1
  1 1         1        0 2
1     1 1     1     0
      0     3 1     1 3
1     1       0
    2 0                3 2
    0     3     0 1     2
  2 0 2       3 2       2
              3
```

62

5 (square)	3 (diamond)	2 (star)	1 (hexagon)	4 (circle)
4 (star)	5 (circle)	1 (diamond)	3 (square)	2 (hexagon)
3 (hexagon)	1 (star)	4 (square)	2 (circle)	5 (diamond)
2 (diamond)	4 (hexagon)	3 (circle)	5 (star)	1 (square)
1 (circle)	2 (square)	5 (hexagon)	4 (diamond)	3 (star)

63 The value of the central letter is the value of the letter in the top left corner plus that in the bottom right corner, also that of the value of the letter in the top right corner plus that in the bottom left corner. Thus the missing value is 13, so the missing letter is M.

64

4	4	4	3	3	1
2	3	3	2	2	1
2	3	3	2	2	1
4	1	1	3	3	1
4	1	1	3	3	1
3	3	3	4	4	2

65

32	16	**20**	25	38	32
34	**27**	29	15	28	30
40	32	27	**21**	12	31
9	48	28	33	17	28
15	21	32	33	32	**30**
33	19	27	36	**36**	12

66 A=136, B=9, C=7, D=10, E=125, F=145, G=16, H=17, I=135, J=161, K=33, L=152, M=194, N=185, O=379.

67

1S	1S	1W	3W	**1W**
3S	1S	1N	1S	1W
2E	3E	■	3W	1S
1E	1E	1S	3W	2N
1E	3E	3N	1N	1W

68

3	**2**	4	1	5
1	4	2	5	3
4	1	5	3	2
2	**5**	3	4	1
5	3	1	**2**	4

69

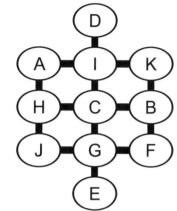

70

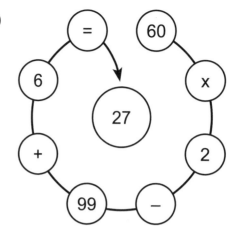

71

2			4			
					4	
	9		2			
9		3				9
				8		
8		9				8

72

4	x	1	x	3	=	12
x		+		–		
7	–	6	x	2	=	2
+		+		+		
9	–	5	x	8	=	32
=		=		=		
37		12		9		

73

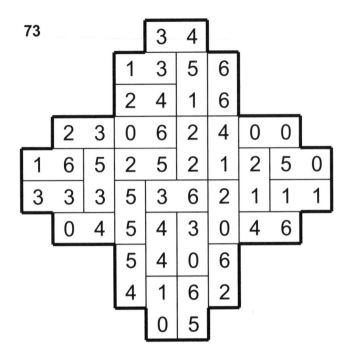

74

75

76

24	17	40	25	15	17	30	19
23	6	13	26	21	29	38	11
32	17	27	22	12	2	10	6
31	22	33	10	18	25	36	39
12	29	8	17	36	28	31	23
1	9	9	27	15	29	12	13
39	24	24	21	20	30	3	14
2	37	17	13	31	23	36	23

77

C	E	D	B	F	A
D	A	B	E	C	F
E	B	F	A	D	C
B	C	A	F	E	D
F	D	E	C	A	B
A	F	C	D	B	E

78

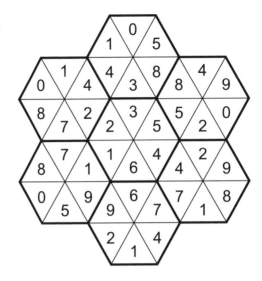

79

80

●	2			0		0		2	●
2	●			2	1		2	●	
		●	●	●	2		●	3	
0		2			●		●	●	2
		1		2		1	3	●	
●			●	●			3	4	3
●	2	1			2		●	●	●
			0	●	3	3	●		
0			●	3	3			2	
	●	2	●		●		2	●	

81

2	5	4	1	3	6
6	2	3	5	1	4
1	6	2	3	4	5
4	3	5	2	6	1
3	1	6	4	5	2
5	4	1	6	2	3

82

C	C	A	B	A	B
A	B	A	B	C	C
B	A	C	A	B	C
B	C	C	A	B	A
C	B	B	C	A	A
A	A	B	C	C	B

83

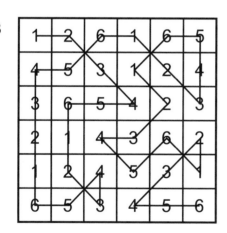

84

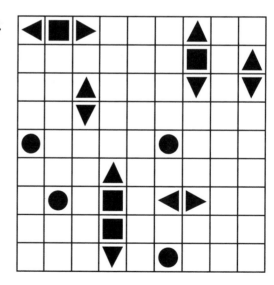

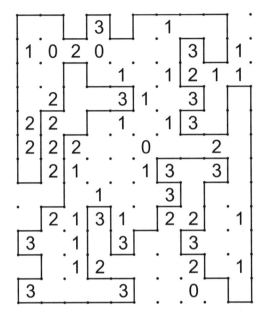

85

86

◇ 1	⬡ 3	▢ 5	◯ 4	★ 2
◯ 3	▢ 4	◇ 2	★ 5	⬡ 1
▢ 2	★ 1	⬡ 4	◇ 3	◯ 5
★ 4	◇ 5	◯ 1	⬡ 2	▢ 3
⬡ 5	◯ 2	★ 3	▢ 1	◇ 4

87 The value of the central letter is the total value of the two letters in the highest boxes multiplied by the total value of the two letters in the lowest boxes. Thus the missing value is 1, so the missing letter is A.

88

1	3	3	2	2	4
4	1	1	1	1	3
4	1	1	1	1	3
4	2	2	1	1	4
4	2	2	1	1	4
2	1	1	4	4	2

89

44	18	30	26	52	**44**
60	35	18	25	39	37
21	**59**	35	51	25	23
57	43	39	**19**	17	39
18	27	**50**	51	39	29
14	32	42	42	**42**	42

90 A=39, B=9, C=12, D=60, E=35, F=48, G=21, H=72, I=95, J=69, K=93, L=167, M=162, N=260, O=422.

91

2E	1S	1W	2S	1W
3E	3E	3S	1W	3S
2N	1S	■	2S	2N
2N	1E	2E	3W	1W
2N	2N	2N	2W	2N

92

4	**2**	3	**5**	1
3	4	2	1	5
2	1	5	4	3
5	3	1	**2**	4
1	5	**4**	3	**2**

93 24 – Add the number to the left to the number at the top and subtract the number to the right to get the number inside the triangle.

94 Circle = 7, cross = 2, pentagon = 1, square = 9, star = 4.

95 46 – The numbers in the vertical columns decrease by 12, 11, 10, 9, 8, 7 and 6.

96

4	x	7	–	9	=	19
–		x		+		
1	x	6	x	3	=	18
x		+		–		
5	+	8	x	2	=	26
=		=		=		
15		50		10		

97

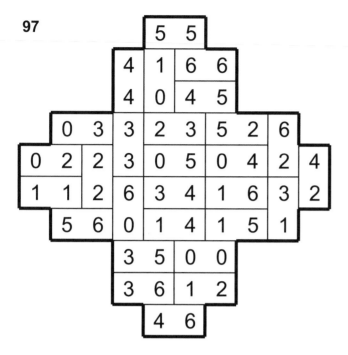

98

99

100

| | | | | | | | 120 |

16	17	23	4	9	11	20	100
10	14	15	7	16	24	13	99
18	5	28	30	1	19	26	127
6	12	14	22	20	13	21	108
2	15	27	17	8	18	28	115
25	16	12	20	24	5	4	106
10	14	26	4	18	19	13	104

87	93	145	104	96	109	125	106

101 The hour hand gains 2, 4, 6, and 8 hours; and the minute hand loses 8, 6, 4, and 2 minutes each time.

102

103

104

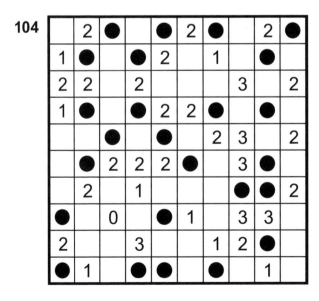

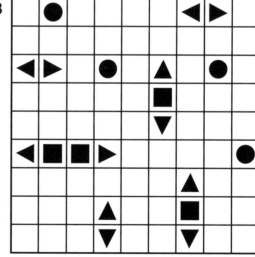

105

1	6	2	5	3	4
2	3	5	6	4	1
6	4	1	3	5	2
4	2	3	1	6	5
3	5	4	2	1	6
5	1	6	4	2	3

106

B	A	C	A	B	C
A	C	B	C	A	B
A	C	B	C	A	B
C	B	A	A	B	C
C	B	A	B	C	A
B	A	C	B	C	A

107

108

109

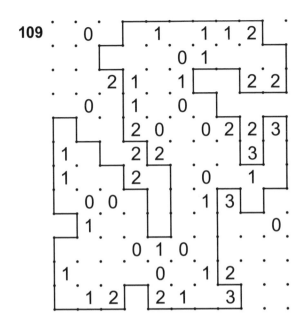

110

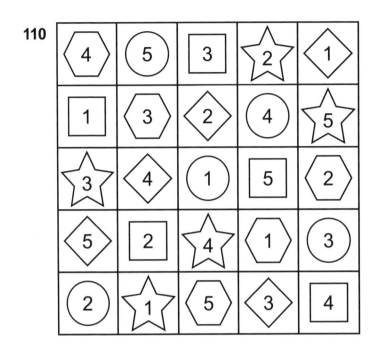

111 The value of the letter in the central square is the difference between the sum total of the values of the letters in the top left and bottom right squares and the sum total of the values of the letters in the top right and bottom left squares. Thus the missing value is 16, so the missing letter is P.

112

1	3	3	2	2	1
4	1	1	3	3	3
4	1	1	3	3	3
2	2	2	4	4	4
2	2	2	4	4	4
4	3	3	1	1	1

113

37	52	**10**	77	51	37
69	66	39	28	20	42
54	20	38	**56**	61	35
35	19	84	12	46	**68**
32	30	57	26	**74**	45
37	**77**	36	65	12	37

114 A=138, B=90, C=86, D=84, E=8, F=228, G=176, H=170, I=92, J=404, K=346, L=262, M=750, N=608, O=1358.

115

2E	2S	2E	3S	1W
1N	1E	2E	2W	3S
3E	3E	■	1N	2W
1N	3N	1W	1E	2W
3N	2E	1W	3W	2W

116

2	3	**1**	4	**5**
4	2	5	**3**	1
3	**1**	**4**	5	2
5	4	2	1	3
1	**5**	3	2	4

117

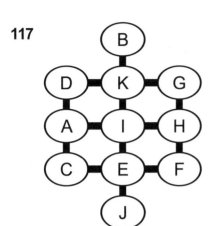

118

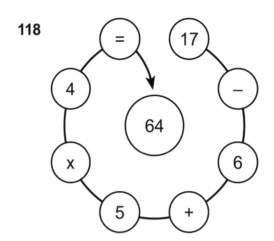

119

9				9		
		4				1
6				6		
		4				6
				7		
	2					7
			8			

120

5	+	3	+	1	=	9
+	■	−	■	+		
4	+	2	x	7	=	42
x	■	x	■	+		
8	x	6	+	9	=	57
=		=		=		
72		6		17		

121

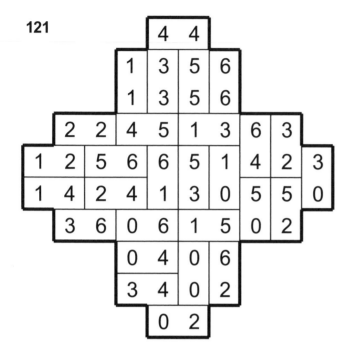

122

●	●		●	
●			●	●
	●			
	●			
	●	●		

123

♡	◇	♣	♠		
		◇	♣	♠	♡
◇	♣	♠	♡		
	♠	♡		♣	◇
♣			◇	♡	♠
♠	♡			◇	♣

124

							118
19	28	5	2	15	18	20	107
6	29	1	27	24	11	19	117
16	21	23	3	1	30	12	106
25	30	6	15	4	14	23	117
27	2	22	26	8	19	3	107
9	28	7	5	12	27	13	101
21	6	14	25	17	23	10	116
123	144	78	103	81	142	100	131

125

C	E	D	F	B	A
E	B	A	D	F	C
D	A	F	B	C	E
A	F	B	C	E	D
B	D	C	E	A	F
F	C	E	A	D	B

126

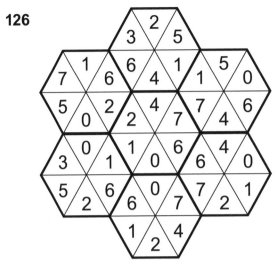

127

128

1		3	●	3	●	3	3	●	
	●		●			●	●	3	1
●	2	3	●	●	3		●		1
2			●	2		1			●
2	●	1							1
●	2		0						
	2		0			1	1	●	
	●	2		3	●	3			
2		●	3	●		●	4	●	1
●		2	●		3	●		1	

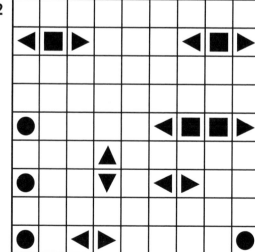

129

4	5	1	6	2	3
1	2	3	5	6	4
2	6	5	3	4	1
3	1	4	2	5	6
6	3	2	4	1	5
5	4	6	1	3	2

130

B	A	C	A	B	C
A	C	A	C	B	B
B	B	A	A	C	C
C	C	B	B	A	A
A	A	C	B	C	B
C	B	B	C	A	A

131

132

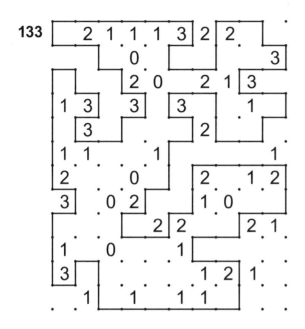

133

134

3 (circle)	4 (hexagon)	5 (square)	2 (diamond)	1 (star)
1 (diamond)	5 (circle)	3 (star)	4 (square)	2 (hexagon)
2 (square)	3 (diamond)	1 (hexagon)	5 (star)	4 (circle)
4 (star)	1 (square)	2 (circle)	3 (hexagon)	5 (diamond)
5 (hexagon)	2 (star)	4 (diamond)	1 (circle)	3 (square)

135 The value of the letter in the bottom right square is the sum total of the values in the top squares minus that of the values in the bottom left and central squares. Thus the missing value is 5, so the missing letter is E.

136

4	4	4	3	3	2
1	1	1	3	3	4
1	1	1	3	3	4
3	2	2	2	2	1
3	2	2	2	2	1
3	1	1	4	4	1

137

38	**5**	33	31	68	48
47	37	**29**	30	38	42
43	56	37	**33**	27	27
37	58	38	41	**8**	41
35	43	53	37	30	25
23	24	33	51	52	**40**

138 A=47, B=18, C=12, D=139, E=73, F=65, G=30, H=151, I=212, J=95, K=181, L=363, M=276, N=544, O=820.

139

2E	1W	2E	3S	1S
3S	1W	2S	1N	1W
1E	2E	■	1W	2S
1E	3N	2W	1S	**1N**
2N	3N	3N	2W	2W

140 Circle = 6, cross = 9, pentagon = 4, square = 7, star = 5.

141 4 – The numbers in each horizontal row total 42, 44, 46, 48, 50, 52 and 54.

142

43	44	49	46	47	17	16
39	42	45	48	18	15	9
38	40	41	19	14	8	10
37	29	31	20	7	13	11
36	30	28	32	21	6	12
35	2	33	27	5	22	24
1	34	3	4	26	25	23

143

2	6	5	8	9	4	0	3	1	7
8	0	2	1	3	7	6	5	9	4
4	7	5	9	6	1	0	3	8	2
3	9	2	1	8	7	6	5	0	4
6	1	5	7	3	4	0	8	9	2
8	0	4	1	5	9	2	3	7	6
31	**23**	**23**	**27**	**34**	**32**	**14**	**27**	**34**	**25**

144

145

6	1	6	6	1	3	4
3	5	3	5	5	2	4
4	5	1	2	0	3	2
1	0	2	5	6	0	1
1	0	3	2	2	3	5
6	5	3	1	0	2	4
3	1	4	5	6	6	0
4	6	4	0	2	4	0

146

147

4	3	6	5	1	2
5	6	3	2	4	1
1	2	4	3	5	6
6	5	2	1	3	4
3	4	1	6	2	5
2	1	5	4	6	3

148

6	1	3	8	5	4	2	7
3	7	6	4	1	2	5	8
8	5	4	1	2	7	3	6
4	2	1	3	6	8	7	5
5	6	2	7	8	3	1	4
2	8	7	6	3	5	4	1
1	4	5	2	7	6	8	3
7	3	8	5	4	1	6	2

149

O	X	O	O	X	O	X	X
O	O	X	X	O	X	X	O
X	X	O	O	X	O	O	X
O	O	X	O	X	X	O	X
X	O	O	X	O	X	X	O
O	X	X	O	X	O	O	X
X	O	X	X	O	O	X	O
X	X	O	X	O	X	O	O

150

1	5	6	4	2	3
3	1	4	2	5	6
4	2	5	3	6	1
5	4	3	6	1	2
2	6	1	5	3	4
6	3	2	1	4	5

151

△	□	○	△	□	△	○	○
□	○	△	□	○	△	□	○
△	□	○	□	□	△	□	□
□	○	△	○	○	□	△	○
○	△	□	△	○	□	△	○
△	○	○	△	△	□	△	○
○	△	○	□	□	△	○	□
□	△	△	○	□	○	□	○
○	○	○	□	△	○	○	△

152

F	B	A	D	C	E
A	C	D	E	B	F
B	F	E	C	A	D
D	E	C	A	F	B
E	A	B	F	D	C
C	D	F	B	E	A

153

4	2	6	1	5	7	3
3	1	7	5	2	6	4
6	7	2	3	4	5	1
1	6	5	7	3	4	2
5	3	1	4	6	2	7
7	5	4	2	1	3	6
2	4	3	6	7	1	5

154

	3	●	●		●	4	●	●
●	●	5	4		●	●	4	●
●	5	●	●			4		2
●		3		●	●		●	1
●	4	●		5	●	5		
●		2	4	●	●	●	3	2
2		●	3	●			●	●
●	3	2			3	2		3
1		●		●	2	●	2	●

155

C	D	E	B	A	C	D	B	E	A
E	A	B	C	D	E	B	A	D	C
B	D	E	A	B	C	E	C	A	D
E	C	B	D	E	A	C	D	B	A
A	B	A	C	D	E	D	B	E	C
D	C	D	A	E	B	A	E	C	B
C	B	C	E	A	D	B	A	D	E
B	E	A	D	C	B	C	E	A	D
D	A	C	E	B	A	E	D	C	B
A	E	D	B	C	D	A	C	B	E

156

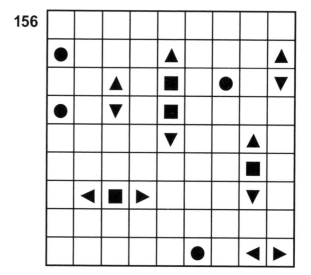

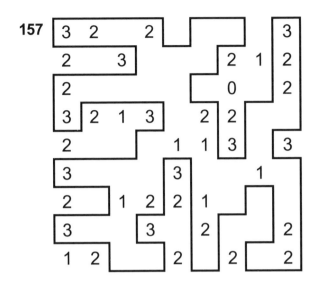

157

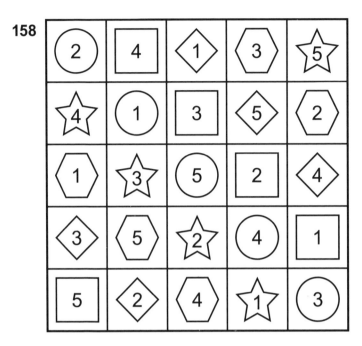

158

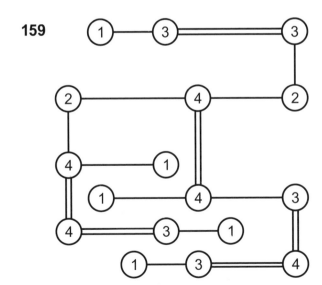

159

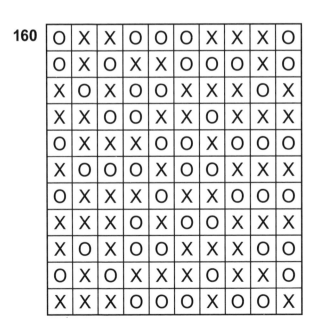

160

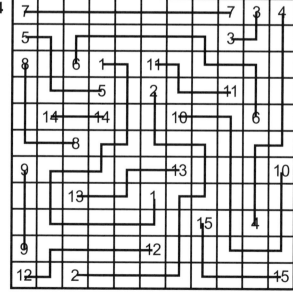

161

6	3	4	2	5	7	1
2	4	1	7	6	3	5
4	6	2	5	7	1	3
5	2	3	6	1	4	7
7	5	6	1	3	2	4
1	7	5	3	4	6	2
3	1	7	4	2	5	6

162

48	47	20	19	17	14	15
33	49	46	21	18	16	13
34	32	45	23	22	12	11
37	35	31	44	24	10	8
38	36	43	30	25	7	9
39	42	29	26	1	4	6
40	41	27	28	3	2	5

163

5	9	2	3	1	4	0	6	7	8
4	7	5	9	0	8	3	2	1	6
9	8	1	4	6	7	5	0	3	2
4	6	3	0	9	2	1	7	5	8
2	5	9	1	7	8	3	4	6	0
3	4	6	5	2	9	0	8	7	1
27	39	26	22	25	38	12	27	29	25

164

165

2	3	1	4	2	2	2
6	3	5	4	2	6	5
1	0	3	1	6	0	0
5	5	6	6	2	0	3
4	6	0	2	5	4	4
6	5	1	5	5	3	4
3	0	0	4	3	3	6
1	2	1	1	1	0	4

166

167

5	3	1	4	2	6
1	6	2	3	5	4
4	2	3	1	6	5
2	4	5	6	3	1
3	1	6	5	4	2
6	5	4	2	1	3

168

6	5	1	2	7	8	4	3
1	4	5	7	8	6	3	2
4	7	2	5	6	3	1	8
2	1	8	3	4	5	6	7
7	2	3	6	5	4	8	1
8	3	6	4	1	2	7	5
3	8	4	1	2	7	5	6
5	6	7	8	3	1	2	4

169

X	O	O	X	O	X	X	O
X	O	O	X	O	O	X	X
O	X	X	O	X	O	O	X
O	O	X	X	O	X	X	O
X	X	O	O	X	O	O	X
O	X	X	O	X	O	O	X
O	O	X	X	O	X	X	O
X	X	O	O	X	X	O	O

170

2	4	3	5	7	6	1
1	3	7	4	6	2	5
3	7	5	2	1	4	6
6	1	2	7	4	5	3
7	2	1	6	5	3	4
5	6	4	1	3	7	2
4	5	6	3	2	1	7

171

172

A	C	B	D	F	E
B	D	C	F	E	A
F	A	E	C	D	B
E	B	F	A	C	D
D	F	A	E	B	C
C	E	D	B	A	F

173

7	3	2	5	4	1	6
5	4	7	6	1	3	2
2	1	3	4	5	6	7
1	5	6	2	3	7	4
3	2	1	7	6	4	5
6	7	4	1	2	5	3
4	6	5	3	7	2	1

174

1	2			●	1		●	1
1	●	●		3		2		2
		4	●	●	3	●	3	●
2	●	3		●	4			●
●	4	●	4	●		3	●	3
3	●	3		●	●	3	●	3
2	●		2		4		3	●
2		2		●	2	●		2
●		●	2			1		●

175

E	C	D	B	A	E	A	C	D	B
A	E	A	C	D	B	E	D	B	C
E	A	B	E	C	D	B	A	C	D
C	E	C	D	B	A	D	B	A	E
D	A	B	E	D	C	A	C	E	B
B	C	D	A	B	E	C	E	D	A
A	B	E	D	C	A	E	D	B	C
C	D	A	B	E	C	D	B	A	E
D	B	E	C	A	D	B	E	C	A
B	D	C	A	E	B	C	A	E	D

176

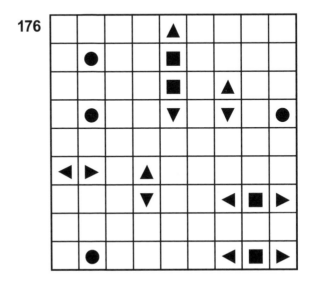

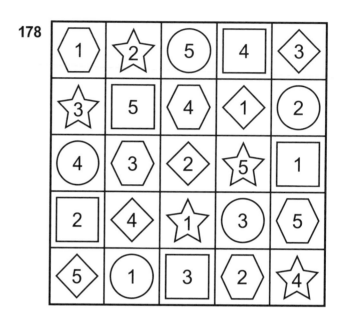

177

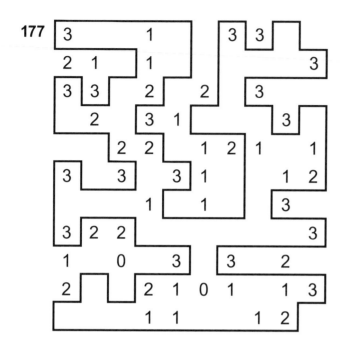

178

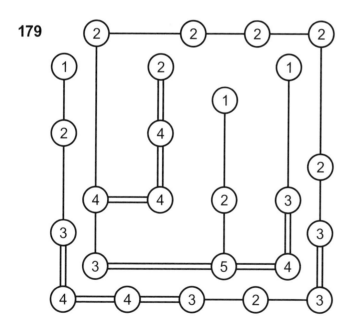

179

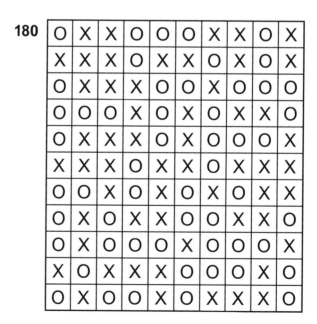

180

181

4	3	1	7	6	5	2
7	1	5	2	4	6	3
6	7	3	4	5	2	1
1	4	7	6	2	3	5
2	6	4	5	3	1	7
5	2	6	3	1	7	4
3	5	2	1	7	4	6

182

6	5	3	2	24	23	19	18
7	63	4	1	25	22	20	17
64	8	62	26	27	13	21	16
60	61	9	11	12	28	14	15
59	58	10	55	29	30	31	32
49	57	56	54	53	39	38	33
48	50	51	52	43	37	40	34
47	46	45	44	42	41	36	35

183

1	9	0	8	4	7	2	3	6	5
4	6	5	1	3	0	9	7	2	8
9	1	3	7	4	8	2	0	6	5
0	2	8	6	1	3	9	5	7	4
3	7	5	4	9	8	2	1	6	0
8	0	9	7	2	6	5	4	3	1
25	**25**	**30**	**33**	**23**	**32**	**29**	**20**	**30**	**23**

184

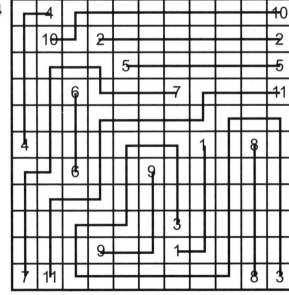

185

2	5	2	7	0	1	1	2
4	3	0	4	5	3	4	2
1	6	7	6	0	1	0	2
7	6	5	4	3	7	5	7
7	6	1	0	2	6	1	4
6	7	6	5	6	5	1	7
3	3	1	3	4	0	2	0
2	6	5	5	0	2	5	7
3	3	3	1	0	4	4	4

186

187

4	7	3	1	2	5	6
2	3	5	6	4	1	7
7	6	4	5	1	2	3
3	1	6	2	7	4	5
6	2	7	4	5	3	1
1	5	2	3	6	7	4
5	4	1	7	3	6	2

188

2	7	8	3	1	4	9	6	5
3	4	7	2	5	8	1	9	6
6	5	1	4	3	2	7	8	9
5	2	3	6	9	1	8	7	4
4	3	9	8	7	6	2	5	1
1	6	5	9	8	7	4	3	2
8	1	2	7	6	9	5	4	3
7	9	4	5	2	3	6	1	8
9	8	6	1	4	5	3	2	7

189

O	O	X	O	O	X	X	O	X	X
X	X	O	O	X	X	O	O	X	O
O	O	X	X	O	O	X	X	O	X
X	O	X	O	X	O	O	X	O	O
O	X	O	X	O	X	X	O	X	O
O	O	X	X	O	O	X	O	X	X
X	X	O	O	X	O	O	X	O	X
O	O	X	X	O	X	O	X	X	O
X	X	O	O	X	O	X	O	O	X
X	X	O	X	X	O	O	X	O	O

190

5	1	3	8	2	4	7	6
7	3	8	6	4	2	1	5
1	6	2	5	8	7	3	4
8	7	6	4	3	5	2	1
2	8	4	3	1	6	5	7
3	5	1	7	6	8	4	2
4	2	7	1	5	3	6	8
6	4	5	2	7	1	8	3

191

192

C	B	D	F	A	G	E
A	G	C	E	D	B	F
G	A	E	C	F	D	B
E	F	G	D	B	C	A
D	E	A	B	C	F	G
B	C	F	A	G	E	D
F	D	B	G	E	A	C

193

5	2	8	4	7	6	1	3
3	4	7	6	5	2	8	1
1	7	6	3	8	5	2	4
6	5	2	8	4	1	3	7
8	3	4	2	1	7	5	6
4	8	1	7	2	3	6	5
2	6	5	1	3	4	7	8
7	1	3	5	6	8	4	2

194

●	●	3	●	2		3	●		1	
4	●	5	2		●	3	●		●	2
2	●	3	●	3				●	6	●
			3	●	2	●	5	●	●	●
2	●	●	3			3	●	●		
●	4	●			●		3		3	●
3			3	2	2	●			●	4
●	●	●	●	●		2		4	●	●
●	●	6	●	●	4		●	3		
4	●		4	●	●	2		●		1
2	●	2		●				●	3	●

195

B	D	A	F	C	E	D	F	C	A	B	E
F	A	B	C	E	D	C	A	D	E	F	B
A	F	C	B	D	C	B	E	F	A	E	D
B	D	E	F	B	E	D	C	A	F	A	C
C	B	F	E	D	F	C	A	E	B	D	A
E	C	A	D	E	A	F	B	D	C	B	F
F	E	D	A	F	C	A	D	E	B	C	B
D	A	B	C	A	B	E	C	F	D	F	E
A	B	C	E	F	D	A	D	B	C	E	F
D	C	E	A	B	F	B	E	A	F	D	C
C	E	F	D	A	B	E	F	B	D	C	A
E	F	D	B	C	A	F	B	C	E	A	D

196

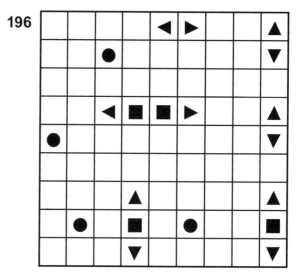

197

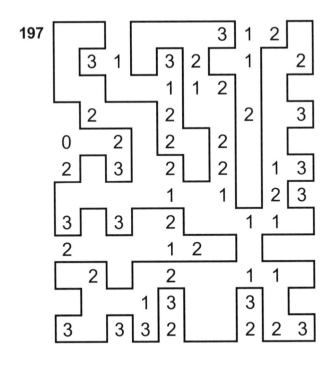

198

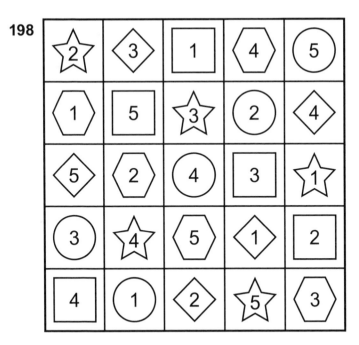

199

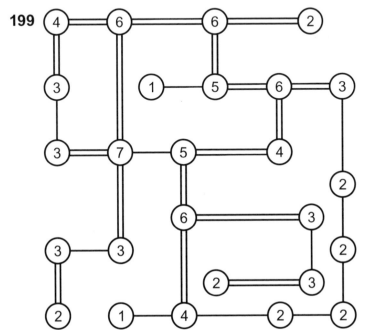

200

X	X	X	O	O	X	O	O	X	X
X	O	X	O	X	X	X	O	O	O
X	O	X	X	X	O	O	O	X	X
O	O	O	X	O	O	O	X	X	O
X	X	O	O	X	X	X	O	O	O
X	O	X	X	X	O	O	X	X	X
O	O	X	O	O	O	X	O	O	O
X	O	O	O	X	X	X	O	X	X
O	X	X	X	O	X	O	X	O	O
X	O	O	X	X	X	O	O	X	X
X	O	X	O	O	O	X	X	X	O
O	O	X	O	X	X	O	X	O	O
O	X	X	O	X	X	O	O	O	X

201

4	7	5	8	1	6	3	2
2	5	1	4	3	8	7	6
5	6	2	3	7	1	8	4
6	8	7	1	5	4	2	3
7	2	3	6	4	5	1	8
3	4	8	7	6	2	5	1
8	1	4	5	2	3	6	7
1	3	6	2	8	7	4	5